CAD PRIMER

COMPUTER-AIDED DESIGN

by

VERNON PAIGE

The Author of **CAD REVEALED**

Instructor, Computer-aided Design
De Anza College
Cupertino, California

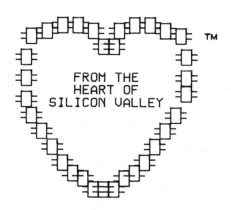

FROM THE
HEART OF
SILICON VALLEY

™

WILD HORSES PUBLISHING COMPANY

Library of Congress Cataloging in Publication Data

Paige, Vernon, 1937-
  CAD primer.

  Rev. ed. of: CAD revealed.
  Bibliography:p.
  Includes index.
  1. Computer Graphics. 2. Engineering Design —— Data
processing. I. Paige, Vernon, 1937-   , CAD revealed.
II. Title.   III. Title: C.A.D. primer.
T385.P34 1985   620′.00425′02854   84-19548
ISBN 0-937148-08-3 (pbk.)

WILD HORSES PUBLISHING COMPANY
12310 CONCEPCION ROAD
LOS ALTOS HILLS, CALIFORNIA 94022
Phone (415) 941-3396

Dedicated to my wife Gerri,
for her support and encouragement

CAD GRAPHICS COURTESY OF:
Apple Computer, Cupertino, CA
Cadam, Burbank, CA
Calma, Sunnyvale, CA
Computervision, Bedford, MA
Gerber Systems, South Windsor, CT
Intergraph, Huntsville, AL
Prime Computer, Natick, MA
Racal-Redac, Westford, MA
Versatec, A Xerox Company,
Santa Clara, CA
Typeset by Techni-Process/ComputerPress, Los Altos, CA
Printed by Thompson-Shore, Dexter, MI

DESIGN, EDITING, & PRODUCTION:

Pam Walatka
Annette Davis
Skip Henderson
Slonaker's
Gene Portugal
Joe Jamello
Roger Cinnamond
Laurel Rezeau
Gary Coombs
Sidney Damon
Jill Jensen
Rain Blockley
Carol Slechta

Jerry Walatka
Nancy Jamello
Brian O'Donnell
Peter Portugal
Jody Main
Bill Main
Patrick Paet
Community Graphics
Dorothy Portugal
Polly Koch
Gene Barnes
Mark Livesay
Hamilton Press

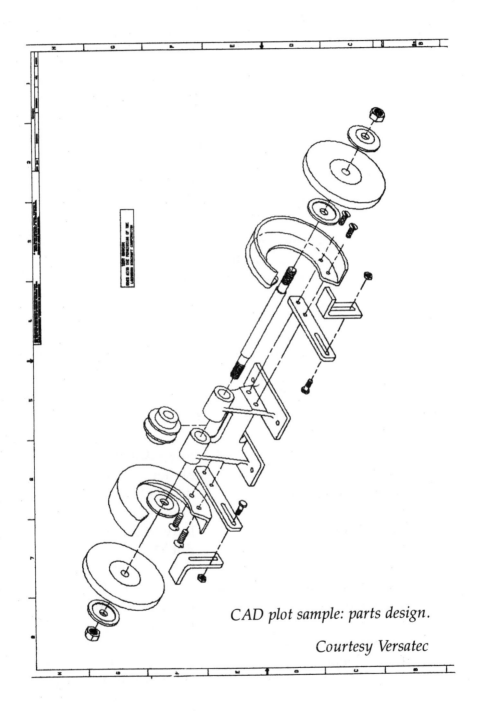

CAD plot sample: parts design.

Courtesy Versatec

CONTENTS

Page

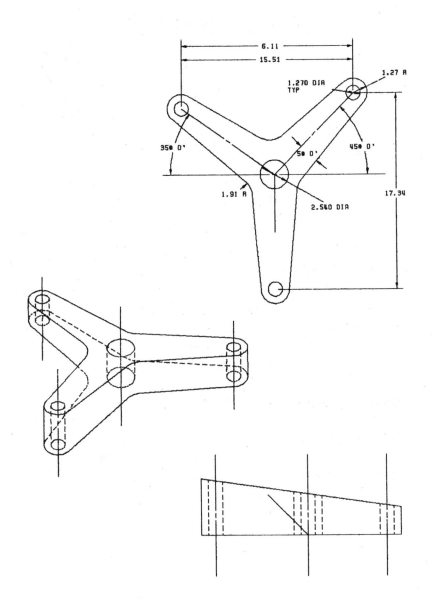

CAD plot sample: machine part, three views.   Courtesy Versatec

CHAPTER ONE
OVERVIEW

1.1   What Is CAD?

Computer-aided design (CAD) is a sophisticated, totally automated drafting system that performs the mundane portions of drafting in a fraction of the time and with greater accuracy and repeatability than has previously been attainable with manual methods.

Drafters create their designs electronically within the CAD system, view the designs on a TV-like display, make miraculously easy revisions, and then let the system draw the design on paper or clear film.

A typical interactive CAD system is a wonderful engineering design and drafting tool. **Interactive** means it works **with** users, in their own way and at their own speed. It means the users need not be programmers or typists.

An efficient interactive CAD system user directs the hardware and software in unison to do the design and drafting "gruntwork." This leaves the user free to try many design solutions.

The CAD system provides an electronic design/ drafting capability which replaces a designer's or drafter's traditional set of tools (symbol, circle and ellipse templates, French curves, splines, pencils, pens, erasers, erasing shields, erasing machines, Leroy lettering templates, beam compasses, bow compasses, drop pens, protractors, 45, 30, and 60 degree triangles, pencil sharpeners, pencil pointers, various scales, and drafting machines).

The user also has constant access to processors and storage units which provide all the capabilities of a calculator and all the reference information of a math library: data are supplied for both trigonometric and geometric construction. Symbols, patterns, drawing segments, minidrawings, and even complete drawings can be stored and reused.

The processors and storage units also allow the user to electronically erase selected portions of previously made CAD drawings, to insert new portions, to shrink or enlarge scalings, to electronically copy portions of other drawings, and to mirror or flop views for clarity.

To accomplish all this, an integrated combination of hardware and software is required.

Hardware includes the metal cabinets, digitizing tables, display devices, keyboards, processors, data disks, and all the other physical parts of the system. The hardware itself does nothing unless activated by a designer/drafter issuing software commands.

Software includes the invisible sets of instructions that control the hardware. Software is usually provided by the CAD manufacturer, already stored on disk packs or magnetic tape, ready for use.

The input, processing, output, and storage hardware elements are interconnected via cables or telecommunications. Interactive CAD is either a stand-alone system or a processor with remote input/output units attached. The complete system includes the interconnected hardware modules and the software.

The hardware part of a CAD system is depicted in the block diagram. Different CAD manufacturers supply different system configurations and use varying component terminology. In some systems each component other than the processor is called a terminal, while other systems have stations and workstations. We have elected to use the term "workstation," since it best describes what is actually being done and where.

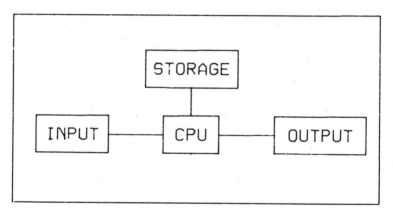

The block diagram.

1.2   Types Of Systems

There are basically two types of CAD systems. In the first, the processor, input, and output modules are interconnected by cables and the software is included and ready to use. This type of system is called a turnkey system. It is called turnkey because, as with an automobile, when you purchase the system, all you need to do is turn it on and start to use it. There is no need to worry about how the system is put together.

In the second type, the software and hardware generally come from different vendors. In most installations the software is purchased and installed on an existing computer system. With this type of system, the user has the responsibility of integrating the hardware and software. This is sometimes called a mainframe system.

1.3   Advantages/Disadvantages

The following is a subjective comparison of turnkey and mainframe CAD systems:

Turnkey Advantages
- Good software support
- Single source of hardware and software
- Easier to use
- Less initial expense
- Vendor handles startup
- All systems not down at once when there is a problem
- Modularity
- Less experienced personnel required
- Common data base
- Security of data base

Turnkey Disadvantages
- Cannot customize, less flexible
- Poor data base management
- No commonality between vendors
- Hard to run third-party software
- Needs many computers for large installation
- Needs large computer for extensive data processing
- Cannot use volume discounts on hardware components
- Slow response time
- Too expensive for large installations
- Limited processing power
- Not good for extensive engineering analysis
- Data base not transportable

Mainframe Advantages
- Can customize system to needs
- Good data base management
- Can develop own software
- Can use third-party software
- Lower terminal cost in large installations
- More workstations per processor
- More processing power for engineering analysis
- Faster response time
- Better interface with non-CAD functions

Mainframe Disadvantages
- Insufficient software
- High initial expense
- Whole system is down at the same time when there is a problem
- Competes with non-CAD functions for processing time
- Requires sophisticated data processing staff
- Service not centralized
- No common data base among third-party software

CHAPTER TWO
HARDWARE

2.1 Processors

The processor, more commonly called the computer, is made of thousands of electronic circuits that can store information and perform various manipulations on that information with incredible speed and accuracy.

Five elements, combined, make up a computer. The primary element, the brains of the computer, is the **central processing unit (CPU).** The CPU performs all the data manipulation; data means information and arithmetic calculations.

Second are the **input and output (I/O)** elements through which data enter and leave the computer. They are much like the eyes, mouth, ears, and hands of a person. The I/O's enable the computer to communicate with the outside world. The input portion accepts the data from the external device — for example, a keyboard or disk — and then prepares them for use by the computer. The output portion accepts the processed data from the computer and prepares them for use by whatever device is electronically connected — a workstation or plotter.

Next, to provide a place to store the required instructions and any data that have been generated, there must be some kind of **memory.** Basically there are two types of memory within the computer: the RAM and the ROM. The acronym RAM is derived from random-access memory, so called because the computer can go right to the information it needs as soon as it determines the right place to look. With RAM, the computer does not have to sort through a large stack of information before finding the appropriate instruction or data. It is like looking for a telephone number in a telephone book and not having to read all the names before finding what you want.

RAM is also called volatile because it can remember the data stored in it only as long as power is applied. Once the power has been removed, the memory promptly forgets, and the next time power is applied it must be taught all over again. This is like having a series of lights, each controlled by a button. When you press down any combination of buttons, the corresponding lights come on. When you release the buttons, the lights go off. All data is stored in the RAM as a series of 1's and 0's, called **bits**.

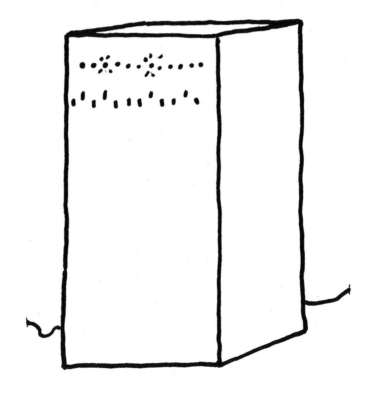

The processor.

This is again like the light bulbs, where a 1 is on and a 0 is off. Eight bits make up a **byte** which is the smallest unit that describes a letter or number. The amount of memory in a computer is measured in bytes. 64K bytes would represent 64 x 1,024 bytes, or 65,536 letters, or about 100 typewritten pages. **K** is a shorthand notation for 1,024.

A ROM (Read Only Memory) is like a RAM whose data are not lost even when the power is turned off. Data cannot be written into it, only read from it. The ROM has many uses. After the power is turned on, the computer must be given detailed instructions, that is, where to get the incoming data (from which peripheral). It must then be fed specific information; that is, what to do with the incoming data — what kind of calculation or other process is going to be done. These instructions can be in the ROM and thus never erased.

The **clock**, which causes things to happen in sequence, is as important an element to the computer as the heart is to the human body. Because a computer is a complex arrangement of digital hardware, marching to the tune of the software, something has to establish the correct beat so that hardware and software can operate in step. Without correct timing all would be chaos. The beat in a computer is generated by an electronic circuit called a clock, which emits an accurately controlled electric pulse at certain prescribed intervals. The clock signal is then passed to all devices. Thus, each one has the same reference.

The final element is the **power supply**, which provides the direct current to the computer. It is like the mouth and stomach feeding the brain.

The computer acts as the master controller and manager of all workstation input and revising, data storage activities, and plotting. It directs the plotter precisely what to draw, copies disk data onto magnetic tapes for semi-active storage, reads magnetic tapes of drawings or documentation for revision or other reuse, and transmits data to and from other computers. It is a veritable chief executive and traffic controller.

The computer usually has a "foreground" and "background" capability allowing it to perform a number of tasks simultaneously. While designs or drawings are being worked on at workstations in the foreground, plotters, tape units, and printers can operate in the background without affecting the speed or accuracy of the design/edit process.

Finally, the CAD computer can be connected to other CAD systems to expand the stored data and processing capacity. It can also be connected to larger host computers to benefit from more elaborate analysis programs, giant data files, and numerical control programs.

2.2   Workstations

The **drafting workstation** is composed of a large, smooth drafting table called a **digitizer** (which converts graphics to digits) and a TV-like **display** with **alphanumeric keyboard**; this is the control center for active work input. The drafter commands all systems functions from this station, seated for smaller drawings or standing to input larger drawings.

The digitizer is wired so that the location of each place on its surface can be sent electronically to the processor by pushing the input button on the crosshair device to indicate a particular point. In the processor, all information is in digits (0 or 1); the digitizer changes graphics (lines and points) to digits. The processor then uses its immense calculating power to change the lines as the user indicates and reproduce them on the TV-like display.

CAD systems have different methods of operation, depending on the manufacturer. Here is a hypothetical example of what a user might do at a drafting workstation. He sits down, types two or three words on his keyboard or selects an area on his digitizer, and the drawing he had been working on yesterday appears on the screen. As he moves the crosshair device across the digitizer table, a little cross (cursor) follows this movement on the screen. When the cursor is on a certain line, he pushes a button marked DEL (delete); the line completely disappears! He pushes LBP (line between points), moves the crosshair device, and digitizes two points by pushing the input button when the cursor is at one end, then the other, of the line he wants; a line appears on the screen. He selects the zoom command and the picture expands. He decides he wants the drawing flopped over. He pushes a few buttons, and the drawing on the screen flops over.

cross-hair device

Drafting workstation: digitizer, keyboard, CRT screen.

Satisfied with his revisions, he selects the save command, and the revised drawing replaces the previous drawing and is stored in the system. He pushes a few more buttons, and his drawing is automatically copied onto paper.

The digitizer can be used to input from a rough schematic or large layout drawing, to input and edit from checkplots, or to perform freehand edits of previously stored drawings. The drafting workstation provides access to the entire CAD system for input and editing of both graphics and text. Drafters find the digitizer not unlike their drafting boards. It even can be tilted, raised, and lowered. Some digitizers are available with backlighting for fast tracing. Some systems provide an instant playback on the display of work in progress in 2-D or 3-D.

Digitizing tablet, with menu and electronic pen.

The **design workstation** is a combination of a touch-sensitive electronic digitizing **tablet, display**, and alphanumeric **keyboard**; this station is the focus for **detail design and revision** (editing) functions. The designer commands all system functions without moving from his or her workstation.

At this station a drawing or a document can be created, revised, and annotated. Graphic items are pinpointed on the display by pointing to an identical area on a companion **tablet** (usually 11″ x 11″) with a hand-held pen-like **stylus**. The display, capable of showing drawing portions enlarged to surprising scales, is like a TV camera which can zoom and pan images so that an American football field can be seen at a 1/30 scale — the equivalent of 12 medium-size drawings.

Design workstation: tablet, keyboard, CRT screen.

All CAD systems use some kind of **display device** to project an image onto a screen. Usually there are two screens, one alphanumeric (letters and numbers), the other graphic (pictures). This image can be produced by a number of available devices.

A popular display device is the **cathode-ray tube** (CRT). It is similar to a television, oscilloscope, or radar. CRTs are available in many sizes and configurations and with various capabilities. The common types of CRTs are described below.

The **vector writing** CRT is similar to Etch-a-Sketch. The computer locates points and then connects the points with lines called vectors. This method is also called **stroke writing**. Vectors are displayed on the screen by a process called **refresh**. Each vector in the picture is restroked so that it appears constantly in view. Thus, a picture is vector-refreshed with each change.

The **raster** CRT uses a grid pattern of dots to display the picture. This is similar to the standard television screen display. Each dot is called a **pixel**.

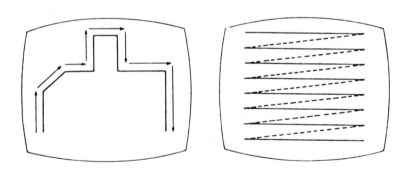

Two types of CRT screens: vector and raster.

The resolution or sharpness of the raster picture is dependent on the spacing of the grid pattern of dots. The smaller the pixels, the more resolution the picture has. The denser the dots, the greater the resolution.

Like the vector writing CRT, the raster CRT refreshes the picture to keep it in view. The picture is refreshed by scanning the grid pattern of dots from left to right and from top to bottom very fast (30 to 60 times per second).

The **storage tube** draws a line on the screen similar to the vector writing CRT but the phosphor on the surface of the screen holds the picture for a very long time. There is no refreshing of the picture.

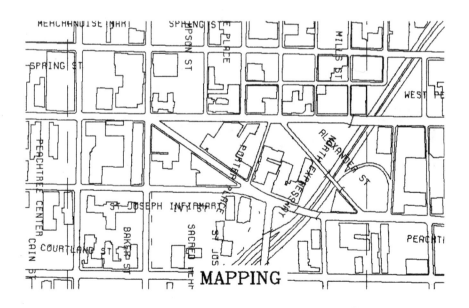

CAD plot sample.   Courtesy Versatec

2.3   Auxiliary Storage

Data may be stored in three ways with interactive CAD: **Magnetic disks** (which are configured like stacked long-playing records but have much more storage capacity) contain data in a form quickly accessible to the system. **Magnetic tapes** (resembling reel-to-reel audio tapes) are used for semi-active storage and are more user accessible and easily transferred. The **computer** itself has a storage capacity, although data is seldom stored there for extended periods.

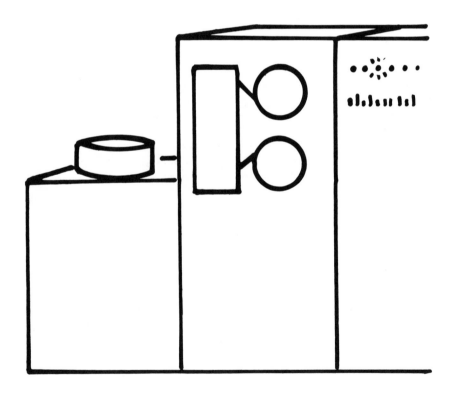

Storage units: disk drive, tape drive, and part of the processor.

System commands, utility instructions, and computational procedures are usually stored on disks. Seldom used reference data is usually stored on magnetic tape.

Symbol libraries, drawing segments, whole drawings, design models, and submodels complete with text are stored on magnetic tape (if inactive or waiting for scheduled revisions) or on disks (if needed for reference at an adjoining workstation or another CAD system).

A completed drawing is placed on a portion of disk storage where it can be found rapidly by the system. Should it be prudent to clear the disk for new work or move the drawing onto magnetic storage, the computer can accomplish the disk-to-tape transfer as a background task.

Anything stored in the system can be copied electronically: disk-to-disk, disk-to-tape, tape-to-disk, tape-to-tape. Hence an off-site fireproof storage vault can store CAD duplicates of all drawings in progress or completed — a luxury not affordable with design office original vellum or mylar drawings in wooden plan files.

Disks are directed by the computer to deliver stored data into its memory for active use in the design/drafting process. They are also directed to record data from various sources, especially workstations.

A **disk drive** keeps the multi-platter disk pack spinning at a very high speed while "catching and recording" data. A complete drawing (digital version) can be moved from the disk to a workstation screen in less than thirty seconds.

One standard reel of magnetic tape can store up to 200 complete drawings. Four rows of magnetic tape shelves store enough reels of tape to store 72,000 drawings — in just a ten-square-foot area. Reduced to microfilm, the same 72,000 drawings can be stored in an area of only one square foot.

2.4   Output

Output from CAD systems can be in many forms. The most common is a drawing just like the one created on a drafting board. This drawing is created by a **plotter**.

Output can also be a copy of what is on the screen, called a **hardcopy**. A hardcopy normally comes from a printer or plotter attached directly to the workstation. A drawing can not only be obtained from a plotter, but can also be drawn on microfilm. This is called **computer output microfilm (COM)**. Output is not always a drawing. Sometimes the output is a magnetic tape containing instructions for a particular machine to make the part that has been designed. This form of output is called **numerical control (NC).** The output could also be a report produced on a line printer. Artwork for printed circuit or integrated circuit design can be produced on a photoplotter.

Although there are many types of plotters available for use on CAD systems, the two most popular types are **pen plotters** and **electrostatic plotters.** The most popular pen plotters are a high-speed drum type and a flatbed type.

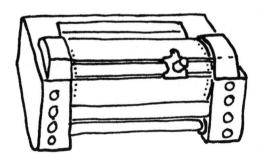

Drum plotter: the paper rolls past a moving pen.

A typical **drum plotter** operates under computer control by rolling paper on a wide drum past axially moving ink pens. Either ballpoint, felt tip, or ink pens may be used. This unit is easy and convenient to use, placing lines on the paper or mylar at rates up to 30 inches per second.

As the name suggests, a **flatbed plotter** has a flat, horizontal drawing surface with the paper lying flat, suitable for highly accurate, top quality drawings. On most flatbed plotters, the pens move and the paper remains stationary. A large flatbed plotter can accommodate up to six drawings at one time. Free-floating or carriage-driven drafting heads can reproduce lines at 20 inches per second at 0.005 inch (0.0125 mm) accuracy and 0.002 inch (0.005 mm) repeatability.

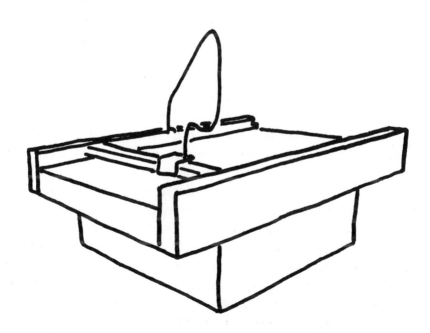

Flatbed plotter: the paper lies flat while the pen moves.

*Electrostatic plotter: the paper moves past stationary electric nibs.
From photo courtesy Versatec*

All **electrostatic plotters** share a similar operating
principle. Electric voltage is applied to an array of densely
spaced writing nibs embedded in a stationary writing head.
The nibs selectively create minute electrostatic dots on the
paper as the paper passes over the writing head. The paper
is then exposed to liquid toner to produce a visible, permanent image. Plotting twenty to thirty times faster than pen
plotters, electrostatics plot a square foot of data in a few
seconds.

COM devices operate similarly to a pen plotter. The
drawing is plotted on 35mm film with a light beam. The
film is then developed to get a reversed negative.

In some applications, such as numerical control,
there is no need to produce a drawing. The description of
the designed part is translated by the computer to instructions for specific machining operations. A magnetic tape
containing these instructions then drives the specific
machine to automatically make the part.

The digitizer graphics tablet can be used with a personal comput-er. The processor and disk drive are combined with the display to form a single unit.   Various plotters can be used. From photo courtesy Apple

2.5   Hardware Summary

The simplified system block diagram shown at the beginning of the chapter can be further interpolated now with the equipment required to accomplish input, processing, and output. All elements of the system operate in concert, providing consistent, dependable, integrated service.

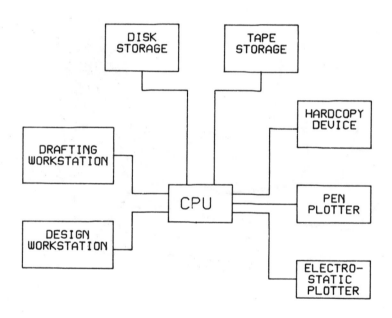

The complete block diagram, showing all the components of CAD hardware.

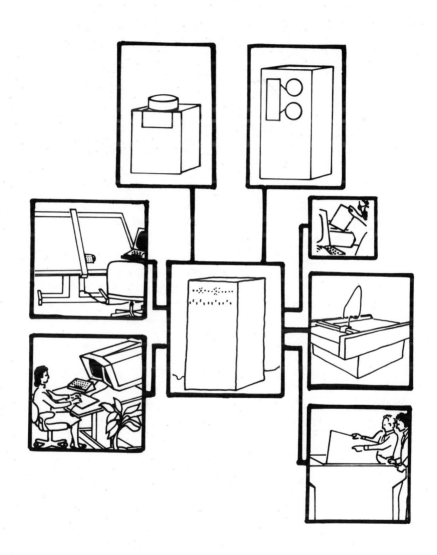

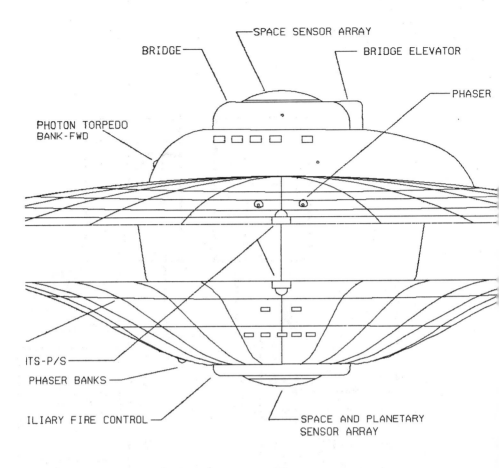

CAD plot sample: spaceship.   Courtesy Intergraph and Versatec

AUTHENTICATED STARDATE	RELEASE DATE 74Ø4.12 7411.Ø1		
MODEL MK-1X	TYPE HEAVY CRUISER	STARSHIP CLASS	
CONSTRUCTED BY	**STAR FLEET DIVISION** SAN FRANCISCO YARDS UNITED NATIONS - EARTH - SOLAR SYSTEM		
ALL DIMENSIONS IN METRIC SYSTEM OF UNITED NATIONS - EARTH			
DRAWN BYı	7312.14	APP'Dı	7312.31
U.S.S. CONSTITUTION CLASS			
SHT OUTBOARD PROFILE		SHT OF	

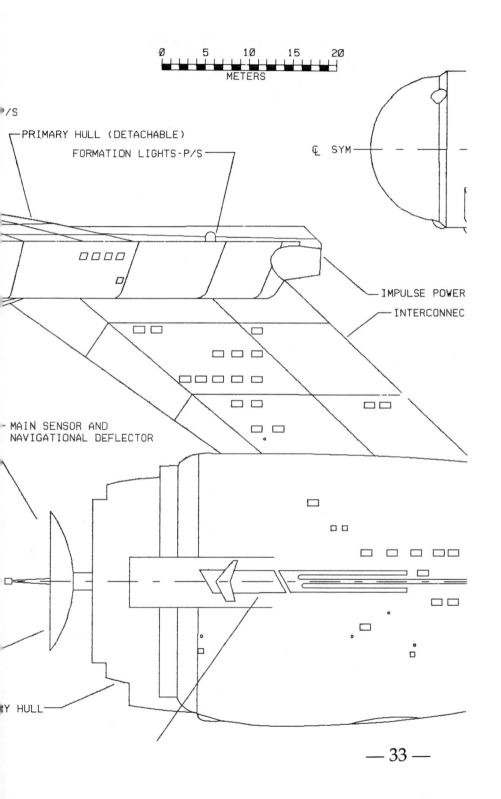

/S

PRIMARY HULL (DETACHABLE)

FORMATION LIGHTS-P/S

℄ SYM

IMPULSE POWER

INTERCONNEC

MAIN SENSOR AND
NAVIGATIONAL DEFLECTOR

Y HULL

CHAPTER THREE
SOFTWARE

3.1   What Is Software?

Software is the programmed instructions that tell the processor what to do. It consists of **programs**, which are magnetic impulses usually stored on tapes or disks. As music is to the familiar tapes and records, so software is to computer tapes and disks.

Programming that is built into the chips (integrated circuits) and printed circuit boards of the computer is called firmware.

Most CAD systems come from the manufacturers already programmed. You do not need to know programming in order to use a CAD system: you just turn it on and the system is ready to use. Such a preprogrammed system is called a **turnkey** system.

Before the days of interactive workstations, software was kept on punched card decks. Imagine the results obtained by the computer operator who dropped a deck of cards or fed them to the computer backwards! Today most interactive CAD systems keep software on their disks, where it is quickly accessible.

Software orders the computer to direct the flow of input data either into working storage or to the disk for instant recall. Software also helps the computer retrieve input data for processing. Software ensures that the computer remembers the formula for volume and center of gravity of, for example, a truncated cone or an engine piston. Software enables the computer to create a drawing out of assorted bits and pieces of points, lines, arcs, circles, ellipses, text, and dimensions. Software makes it possible to calculate square areas, volumes, and intersections of multiple curved surfaces in space. Software queues the plotter to plot different drawings of various sizes in specific order, without the user giving further instructions. Software remembers CAD user passwords (for security) and prevents unauthorized use of the data.

In short, software is the internal operator of any interactive CAD system. It is a binary-based set of programs that operates the system and makes alphanumeric data, geometric data, and picture data all come together for the design and drafting process.

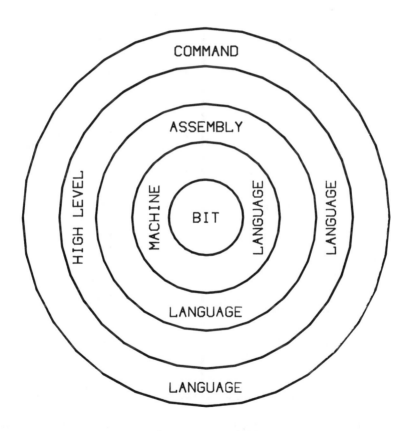

The software onion.

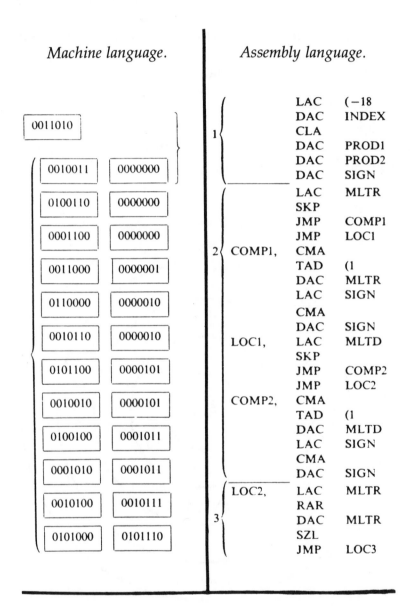

	LAC	(−18
	DAC	INDEX
1	CLA	
	DAC	PROD1
	DAC	PROD2
	DAC	SIGN
	LAC	MLTR
	SKP	
	JMP	COMP1
	JMP	LOC1
2 COMP1,	CMA	
	TAD	(1
	DAC	MLTR
	LAC	SIGN
	CMA	
	DAC	SIGN
LOC1,	LAC	MLTD
	SKP	
	JMP	COMP2
	JMP	LOC2
COMP2,	CMA	
	TAD	(1
	DAC	MLTD
	LAC	SIGN
	CMA	
	DAC	SIGN
LOC2,	LAC	MLTR
	RAR	
3	DAC	MLTR
	SZL	
	JMP	LOC3

From DigitalSystems: Hardware, Organization and Design, by F.J. Hill and G.R. Peterson, pp. 33, 366; Wiley and Sons, NY, 1973.

3.2 Machine Language

Programs written in strings of binary 1's and 0's (called bits) are known as **machine language** programs. All programs must ultimately be placed in this form, since these are the only kinds of instruction the computer can interpret. Writing programs in this form is incredibly difficult. First, binary strings are cumbersome, inconvenient, and downright unnatural to humans. Second, the programmer must assign binary addresses (a storage location for information) to all the data and instructions, and, even worse, keep track of all these addresses.

Software initially developed in a fairly natural and straightforward manner but recently became quite complex. As noted, binary strings are inconvenient, if only because they are so long. It was thus a natural first step to convert instructions to **octal** form, treating each group of three bits as a binary number, and replacing each group with the equivalent octal digit. It was a simple matter to equip the computer with the capability of converting each octal digit to the equivalent binary form.

3.3 Assembly Language

Once we recognize that the computer can convert from one form to another, it is quite natural to replace the number codes with mnemonic names, such as ADD, MULT, DIV, etc., and write a program to enable the computer to convert these names to the equivalent codes. Next, as we assign variables to memory locations, we make up a table giving the addresses corresponding to the variable names. In the address portion of the instructions we simply write the variable name instead of the actual address. When we feed the program into the computer, we also feed in the address table and let the computer replace variable names with the appropriate addresses.

Next we note that assigning addresses is a routine bookkeeping job, just as well given to the computer. Now our programs need contain little more than instructions consisting only of operation names and variable names. At this point we have an assembly language. The program that assigns the addresses and converts the instructions to machine language form is known as an **assembler.**

3.4   High-Level Language

Assembly language is an immense improvement over machine language, but there are still many problems. The main problem is that an assembly language is computer oriented. Each assembly language statement corresponds to one machine language statement, so that the programmer must be familiar with the instructions and internal organization of the particular computer. Knowledge of how to program one computer will be of little value in programming any other computer. We would prefer a language in which we could write programs that could be run on virtually any computer. This leads us to the concept of high-level languages, such as FORTRAN, PASCAL, COBOL, and BASIC.

High-level languages permit us to write programs in forms as close as possible to the natural, "human-oriented" languages that might be appropriate to the particular problems. Thus, a complicated mathematical formula may be evaluated by a single statement in FORTRAN.

The evaluation of a complicated formula will obviously require many machine language instructions. There are two distinct methods for converting high-level language programs into machine language programs within the computer. In one method, as the program is executed, each high-level language statement is converted into a corresponding set of machine language instructions, which are

```
10      DIMENSION X(1000), Y(1000), ...
40      CALL INGDS(I2250, IGDS1)
41      CALL INGDS(I2250, IGDS2)
42      CALL INGDS(I2250, IGDS3)
50      CALL SDATL(IGDS1, 0.0, 0.0, 1000.0, 1000.0)
60      FORMAT( ... )
70      READ (5, 60) A
80      RADIAN = A*3.1416/180.0
90      DO 120 N = 1, 1000
100     T = 0.01*FLOAT(N)
110     X(N) = (400.0*COS(A))*T
120     Y(N) = (400.0*SIN(A))*T – 16.*T**2
130     CALL PPNT(IGDS1, X, Y, ..., ..., ..., 1000)
140     CALL EXEC(IGDS1)
141     CALL CRATL(I2250, IATL)
142     CALL ENATN(IATL, 34)
143     CALL SLPAT(IGDS2, ...)
144     CALL SLPAT(IGDS3, ...)
145     FORMAT ( ... )
146     READ (5, 145) SWEND
147     FORMAT ( ... )
148     READ (5, 147) SWRDA
150     CALL PTEXT (IGDS2, SWEND, 3, 1, ..., 1, 100.0, 800.0)
165     CALL EXEC(IGDS2)
170     CALL PTEXT(IGDS3, SWRDA, 6, 1, ..., 1, 100.0, 700.0)
175     CALL EXEC(IGDS3)
180     CALL RQATN(IATL, IDATN, 2, LPPTR, ..., 34)
190     IF(IDATN–34) 180, 200, 180
200     IF(LPPTR(1) – IGDS2) 210, 220, 210
210     IF(LPPTR(1) – IGDS3) 180, 70, 180
220     ...
        CALL EXIT
```

Fortran, high-level language.   From Interactive Graphics for computer-aided Design, by M. David Prince, p.194; Addison-Wesley, Reading, MA, 1971.

executed immediately, before proceeding to the next high-level language statement. A system functioning in this manner is known as an **interpreter.**

Interpreters are inefficient for programs with repetitive loops. For example, in FORTRAN we use "DO" loops to apply the same set of instructions over and over to a whole set of data. An interpreter has to translate the instructions in the "DO" loop on every pass through the loop, which is clearly inefficient since the translation is the same on every pass. This fault is corrected by **compilers,** which translate the entire high-level language program into a machine language program before it is executed.

Since interpreters and compilers translate into machine language, they must be written separately for each computer. However, the compiler or interpreter for a given language may be written for any computer having adequate memory capacity to hold the software. Thus, programmers writing in a popular language, such as FORTRAN, can run their programs on practically any computer.

3.5   Command Language

In order to interact with the computer, the designers and drafters must communicate their desires via a special command language. The words that make up this language are called **mnemonics.** Mnemonics are short words that can represent complete sentences or phrases of instruction needed to achieve the desired results. The command language is determined by the system manufacturer and can be augmented as the user's needs dictate. As an example of mnemonics in use, consider the following: a user calling up a drawing from storage can direct the system to display all of the lines and curves of the drawing with the mnemonic DISLIN.

Mnemonics can be specified from either the workstation keyboard or digitizer menus. The workstation

AI&C MENU	P410 MENU	PIPING MENU	STPFL MENU		TPG	TAB	LDR		·	CARR RETURN	=	/	" .	^ .	√ #	UCS		
REP	SAR	RPL	TAM	TAO	TEXT START	NAME START	SID	F	L	R	X	LOWER CASE	&	IC2				
CMP	RAD	PAR	PRP	AMG	VPP	VRL	TXO	E	K	O	W	UPPER CASE	:	UBL				
OFF	DIA	+	E	°	END		TXN	D	J	P	V	BLANK	- ..	BKP	DK1			
ON	PRF	-	3	6	9		SEX	C	I	O	U	BLANK	- +	MRF	TXN			
CLO	PRN	.	2	5	8	BACK SPACE	TOL	B	H	N	T	Z	- %	MRF	TXN			
RVP	MDF	0	1	4	7	RE-START	ORG	A	G	M	S	Y	- $	MTX				
ALN	MDN	DR	DA	DX	DY	DZ		RFN	OOH	OOV				MTL	ASC			
	STZ	R	A	X	Y	Z		GLB	BDH	BDV	BDP	DAL	DAP	MRD	NME	TX1		
PDN	PVR	PHV	PDG	PND	PIN	PCR		GNT	DMH	DMV	DMP	DMR	DMD	MDM	TED	DRM		
DRW	USR	MIR	LPT	VER	DSP	C/C												
WIN	SLO	PIC	GRP	EXS	SEL			MIII	MVL	MBP	MCR		GRD	DVP	XIT	FEH		
		OTL	DIR	SYM	MOL	NER		BLK	UBK			STR	WCS	PLT	LST			
TRM	MAG	SCF	ALL	UP	DWN	REPAINT		ACT	MES	DEL	OTL		CLS	ITM	PLR	LWT		
TPO	RTO	CCW	RTN	RTP	ROT			CON	SPL					FHT	UFT			
VPA	PIA	ZVL	LCO	ZTL	ZTC	PSF		CRC	CTP	CCC	CTN		FIL	FSL	PJC			
DUP	NUM	VOL	PLY	CHN	REL	REJECT		LBP	LCP	LHL	LVL	LPL	LTN	LTP	VER	CLR		
TRM	NTM	MAJ	PLN	MOD	ADD				SRV	SRL		SCY	SBS					
MISC OP	MODEL VERIFY		TTO	DGN	DGF			SNT	SPJ	SOF	SFL							
MPTP	MTDC	MPPK	NABP	MCT	MASM	MMDL												
MELE	MXHT	MSHF	MTN	MSYM	MSAS	MANY	STOP	HELP	FILE				DCM	TPG	TAB			
MPNT	MLIN	MARC	MCON	NSPL	MGNL	MDIM							XCT	MCE	TPG	FED		

Photocopy reduction of CALMA's DDM menu.   The menu fits over a portion of the digitizer tablet.   Courtesy CALMA

keyboard is arranged like that of a typewriter. The user types in the mnemonic and hits the "return" button instructing the computer to execute the command. The digitizer **menu** consists of several areas on the digitizer to which mnemonics have been assigned. By digitizing a point within a menu area with the cursor, the user initiates the specified command.

Symbols and subdrawings that have been generated by the user can also be retrieved using the menu. The two are distinct in that symbols are simple drawing entities, such as a flange, that are stored in a library. If the library definition of a symbol is revised, every subsequent appearance of the symbol, in both existing and future drawings, reflects the revision. Subdrawings can be altered independently, as they are used without affecting the record in storage.

MENU FOR MASLIB

BLOB	C1	C5	T1	T2	T3	ENDS	BAR	DIOO	POINT	TRB	TRA	NOC	T4	NCC
PSO	PSC	NEF	LOO	FUSE	LOC	BST	BSP	BEP	TSO	TSC	REL	CNT	LNK	ARO
COR	LMP	NOR	NCR	SOL	TFR	CBR	MCB	CT	FCB	PLUG	ISOL	LSO	LSC	FSO
FSC	DOFREL	DONREL	LATREL	CROSS	FSW	INSIGN	CHKV	TRC	BOX	GAV	GLV	PLV	BALLV	DIAPHM
V2	V3	V4	RV	PRV	NV	ODV	CVOP	SV	CVPP	BUV	REF2	PUMP	BLOWER	WIGGLE
REC	CCL2	HALF	JL	TOGGV	POCV	BO	EWN	CHGV	DV	RES	VRES1	VRES2		

Symbols: menu for master library.   *Courtesy Prime*

3.6   Special Features

Macros: Macros are custom commands that can be created and assigned to a menu. Macros, consisting of sequences of standard graphics commands, allow repetitive, standard, or highly specialized operations to be preprogrammed and then executed with single instructions.

The sequence of commands required to perform a task is entered in the precise order as in the interactive mode. This sequence is then given a unique name which is used as a custom command.

Design Languages: To develop advanced software features, the designers need a design language with which they can call up and execute programs to be used during a design process to reduce repetitious efforts. The design language is a high-level language that is easy to use and understand.

The design language allows the user to write programs in a language such as BASIC or FORTRAN. These programs can access the stored information, read the digitizer, and drive the graphics display.

Analysis Capabilities: The types of analyses needed by the user are as varied as the applications for which the system is being used. Most of the analyses can be done using the high-level language that is available with the system. This will enable the user to customize the system.

Accounting: The system keeps a log of time spent on the system by user, project number, and drawing number. This information is determined automatically from the log-on log-off times.

File Security: File protection is inherent within the system. The protection features include: no entry into the system without the proper password, some data can be viewed but not modified, and certain commands will not be executed until the user has a chance to verify his or her intentions.

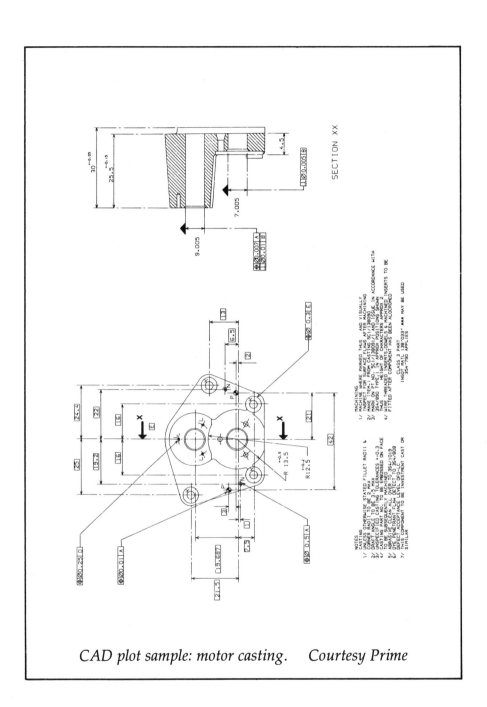

CAD plot sample: motor casting.   Courtesy Prime

CHAPTER FOUR
IMPLEMENTATION

4.1   Getting Started

Many managers planning the acquisition of a CAD system for the first time become uncomfortable about how their people will respond and how well the organization as a whole will react to the transition from traditional to computer-aided engineering methods. Compounding a manager's anxieties are the high expectations — built up during numerous sales presentations and field trips — of supervisors and fellow department heads who look for spectacular turn-around times and better quality work.

Many tough human and psychological questions have to be answered when planning a first installation: Should experts be hired? How quickly will the staff learn? Will any employee fall by the wayside? How will job descriptions and pay scales be affected? Will there be any union or morale problems? Who should be in charge? How closely should the systems be controlled?

Unfortunately, there is not much time to maneuver. Without doubt, what happens in the first six months after a system is delivered is critical to the success of the transition to CAD, particularly in a manufacturing environment. Moreover, early mistakes make strong impressions that are difficult to correct later. It is a fact that a significant number of CAD systems that fail do so because of a lack of adequate planning and management attention to how the technology affects both individuals and organizations.

Some managers about to take delivery of their first CAD system become overwhelmed. First, there is the pressure to be ready before the system arrives. Often, there are conflicting recommendations by various interest groups within the company. Also, there is the formidable, and frequently confusing, jargon used by the vendor. Small wonder, then, that many companies opt for hiring CAD specialists to advise them on how to make the transition smoother.

Many companies make the change-over successfully without the help of specialists, while others fail despite the efforts of newly recruited CAD experts. To understand how this can happen, it is necessary to look at the activities that take place before, during, and after the transition to CAD, the different kinds of specialists, and the contribution they can make.

Prior to the arrival of the system, a lot of planning will be necessary to establish the place of the CAD system in the organization and to set guidelines for the transition to CAD methods. This planning will involve such people-related activities as how the system will be controlled, who will have access, scheduling workstation use, training, hiring, and the tasks to which the system will initially be assigned. This planning will, of course, require an intimate familiarity with the organization and its work. A knowledge of CAD is also needed and this is where the vendor's management advisors can help.

A CAD system is usually purchased to increase the productivity of an engineering or drafting department with the expectation of increasing its output. Most managers want to establish the system's credibility quickly to quiet the doubters and overcome CAD's lingering expensive-toy image. Typically, a small number of simple tasks are chosen for the system. Because the tasks were previously done in different ways by different people, choices have to be made and methods rationalized so that no undesirable items are promulgated inadvertently.

As more tasks are moved to the system, their associated patchwork of guidelines, standards, and procedures will have to be reviewed and rationalized. It is important that the review teams not get bogged down in a massive house-cleaning effort, but concentrate on an area in which the system will quickly show its benefits.

If a CAD management specialist is used, there is little he can do directly during this phase because the knowledge required is mainly about the company and its work. His major role is that of consultant to the planning team, advising them on the planning strategy, the decisions that will have to be made, and the capabilities and performance of the system itself.

Once the system is installed, there is pressure to make it productive as quickly as possible. Initially, a considerable portion of the system's time will be taken up by training sessions and familiarization exercises for new operators. Within a few weeks, most of the workstation time will be devoted to productive work. CAD system operators with well-developed workstation skills can be helpful at this stage, both to accelerate the training of others and to turn out useful work themselves.

Unfortunately, in many cases newly hired specialists have difficulty understanding their engineering tasks and company documentation standards and must be trained in these aspects of their work. Since it is usually more convenient to instruct how to operate a CAD system than to teach an outsider about company operations, most companies prefer to train their existing engineering staffs in CAD rather than hire outsiders and tie up their own people teaching them the firm's systems and documentation.

After the system has been operating successfully for a while, a need often develops for some special capabilities or functions not available in the standard system. Often, advanced programming is required to implement the necessary enhancements. This kind of job is sometimes handled in-house, but many users must go to the vendor or a CAD software specialist to get the work done. Developing these types of skills in-house is unrealistic for a small, one-time job, as it requires a programming background and can require intensive study to learn the detailed workings of large amounts of existing and usually complex software. However, companies that continually need to make extensive changes to their systems can justify two or more of these people on their staffs.

Should it be decided to hire CAD specialists for any reason, it is important to appreciate the different kinds of expertise available and select the right kind of expert for the job at hand. Basically, there are three kinds of specialists: 1) ones who have workstation operator skills, with or without an ability to teach; 2) ones who know the system functions internally and can make modifications and enhancements to its software; and 3) ones with a management orientation who know what plans to make, know how to obtain the most from a system, and have the maturity and judgment to select a proper course of action. Unfortunately, consultants are rarely able to keep up their skills in more than one of these categories.

4.2   Training

Managers look to the vendors' training programs for two results. First, they expect their people to learn about the system and gain the necessary skills to put it into production quickly. Second, they expect an appreciation of CAD's potential that will win over the staff and make them more ready to accept the change in work style and organization that CAD brings. The leading vendors understand these expectations and the influence they have, not only on getting the system into production quickly, but also in getting it accepted psychologically by the people who will have to use it.

Psychologically, the majority of engineers and drafters look forward to CAD training. As a rule, technical people are intrigued by computer graphics and are eager to get their hands on a system. Some look at training as an opportunity to find out more about computers and learn a new skill; others see it as a professional step up and a way to avoid technical obsolescence; a few are excited by the possibility that the drudgery will go out of their work, and many feel it's just plain fun. But a few, typically older professionals, who grew up before the push-button age, feel insecure and harbor doubts about their ability to learn new ways of doing things — though most of them have nothing to worry about.

The great majority of people can learn to be proficient CAD users in less than six months. All levels of technical and some nontechnical professionals have been successfully trained to operate workstations. Engineers, drafters, tracers, illustrators, artists, students, technicians, clerks, and secretaries have become competent operators. Those who fail are usually persons who are inept mechanically or persons who don't think logically.

Numerous polls of vendors and users indicate that most persons develop adequate proficiency in three months and become skilled operators in only six months. Furthermore, most of those polled reported that persons with a moderate amount of aptitude go on to become expert operators after nine months of experience.

It appears that less than ten percent fail to develop even marginal skills and, frequently, this is a result of lack of interest, not ability. Fortunately, these people are not hard to spot. Another ten percent seemingly lack the aptitude to become more than marginal operators. Of the remaining eighty percent, more than half become very good, and the rest experts.

The training offered by vendors varies widely, both in quality and quantity. Some offer courses at the buyer's site only and use the newly purchased equipment in the course. Other vendors hold a regularly scheduled series of coordinated courses on their premises in well-equipped classrooms and laboratories.

The better courses are structured affairs given by full-time professional instructors. Class size is usually limited so that no more than two or three students share a terminal. Ideally, the instructor is knowledgeable about a broad range of CAD, design, and drawing-office subjects.

Off-site learning facilities are preferable because of the interruptions and distractions that invariably occur at the user's plant. Typically, the time is split evenly between classwork and hands-on equipment operation. The better courses also have audio-visual aids, class notes, and tutorial workbooks.

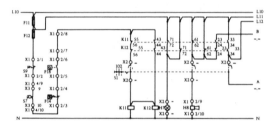

Timing the training sessions can be important. The best time to undergo training is immediately before the system is installed so newly learned skills can be put into practice before they are forgotten. Managers should make the effort to coordinate training with installation of the system.

In addition, timely training will allow the staff to better appreciate the acceptance tests and to work the system for a greater proportion of the warranty period.

Usually there are separate courses for managers, programmers, and operators. Courses designed for operators generally take one or two weeks to complete and are aimed at two or three levels of students. Typically, there is an entry-level course and a number of more-advanced courses intended for people with two to six months' experience. Programming courses also take from one to two weeks and are aimed at experienced programmers or advanced operators. Management courses are tailored to individual needs but are usually given prior to installation planning. In addition, management seminars are held from time to time for more-advanced users and deal with topical issues.

Some representative course titles and their subject matter are outlined below:

- Basic Operator's Course. Entry-level course designed to teach basic skills: turning the system on and off, workstation component operation, command structure, graphics creation and editing commands, on-line storage, magnetic tape, elementary dimensioning, text insertion, function menu design.

- Advanced Operator's Course. Operator's course designed to teach advanced commands and techniques to operators with about three months experience: data structures, data extraction for bill-of-material and other reports, numerical control manufacturing tape generation, parts-properties extraction.

- Applications Course. Engineer's or operator's course designed to teach how to use specialized analysis, report generating or other design or manufacturing applications software packages.

- Applications Programming Course. Programmer's or advanced operator's course designed to teach how to design, code, debug, and install special-purpose programs in a graphics design language: language structure, statement format, vocabulary, operating system interface, program entering, program editing, program compilation, program installation and execution, program debugging, program storage.

- Management Course. Manager's course designed to teach the elements that go into pre-installation planning and system management: workstation layout, lighting, access scheduling, personnel selection, personnel training, hiring, wage scales, labor/management relations, career paths in CAD, high-productivity environment creation.

CAD plot sample: Byrd's String Quartet.   *Courtesy Versatec*

4.3   Personnel Considerations

Manufacturers acquiring CAD equipment for the first time cannot afford to ignore the attitudes of trade unions and, where possible, should seek their support. This is especially true in older industries where unions are extremely influential.

To date, union experiences with CAD have been good and no discernible nationwide union opposition has emerged. If anything, unions are cautiously optimistic about CAD, and it isn't unusual to find union members working with management to promote the technology. However, it is still too early to tell what long-term effects CAD will have on union objectives and individual members. In the mechanical area, where unionization is widespread, CAD has not yet matured and management's approach to it varies from place to place.

Many union members understand and believe in the promise and benefits of CAD and have a deep concern for, and commitment to, the viability of the U.S. manufacturing industry. Few see it as a threat to the union's basic interest of protecting jobs and improving working conditions, pay and benefits.

Job security is, of course, a prime union concern. So far, CAD has not been a job threat. This might surprise some who see CAD primarily as a labor-saving device but, for one thing, there have not been any wholesale conversions to CAD.

Secondly, there have not been spectacular labor savings in all areas. Of course, there have been extremely successful installations and reasonable pay-offs, but gains in productivity have been moderate and slow in coming, overall.

Thirdly, experience indicates that CAD purchases do not result in lay-offs because CAD is something that growing, dynamic companies purchase to ease growing pains or to establish a position of leadership. Even if expanding companies do realize substantial labor savings, they are absorbed in growth. Stagnant or shrinking corporations seldom invest large sums in new, leading-edge technology unless they perceive they cannot survive without it. Quite often, CAD justification on the basis of staff reductions turns out to be a paper exercise.

Finally, because of a shortage of trained drafters, many companies are simply reluctant to let them go.

While the great majority of drafters feel secure in their traditional role in the engineering office and don't anticipate that CAD will change that, a few fear being squeezed by engineers from above and by clerks and computer operators from below. Though this may appear to have happened at some installations, it is not a general trend and should occur less in the future.

Early systems were quite limited in scope and could be operated efficiently by casual operators, such as engineers or technicians or even low-level clerks. At some locations, engineers would do some of the drafting job and clerks would do the work previously done by tracers. But today's systems are more complex, and many users have found that it is not very efficient to allow casual walk-up usage. As CAD develops further and becomes still more complex, full-time professional operators will be required in each engineering specialty, and operators with the types of creative engineering skills possessed by drafters will be in high demand.

Working conditions as a whole seem to have improved at most CAD installations. Usually an office remodeling takes place, and management is concerned about creating a pleasant, productive environment. Many engineers and drafters describe CAD as another tool, like a drafting machine or an ink pen, that makes their job more satisfying.

Pay and benefits have not generally been changed by CAD, but the trend is definitely towards increases. People training in-house are usually not granted raises immediately, but people with CAD skills are in great demand at ever higher salaries.

If this trend continues, drafters with CAD skills can expect higher pay, especially as they gain the potential for being very productive. CAD will, in time, lead to a reduced work week and higher pay for all technical, design, and manufacturing employees.

CAD deserves the support of both management and labor and will not succeed without it. Doubtless, knowing managers will try to understand union sensibilities and make every effort to sell the virtues of the technology to the rank and file.

CAD has had a good influence on staff morale, and it appears that those without access to it are beginning to feel left out in the cold. As CAD becomes less exotic, more and more people see their involvement with it to be inevitable. The increasing number of articles in trade and professional journals and the impressive demonstrations at trade shows reinforce this feeling to the point where most professionals are eager to apply CAD to their work. Indeed, some are anxious that their continuing lack of CAD skills might hurt their careers. CAD has progressed to the point where distinct negative feelings have emerged among those who have not had the opportunity to work with it.

There is a feeling of personal pride and satisfaction in those workers who are proficient with CAD. Results and gratification seem to come quickly and easily. Many users feel a sense of liberation from the laborious repetitive work that can numb the mind and inhibit creativity.

It is important to keep in mind, though, that intense frustration can develop when things don't go right. A bug in software or a machine that's down can get users depressed and downright hostile.

If the experience of computer use in general is any guide, the real morale problems will be based on how well the system works, who is allowed access, and keeping equipment up-to-date.

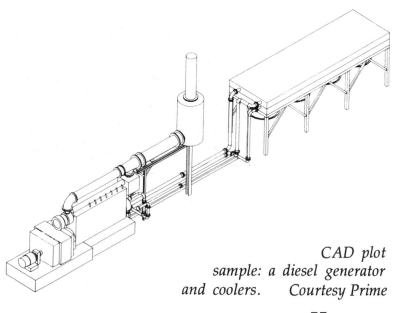

CAD plot sample: a diesel generator and coolers.   Courtesy Prime

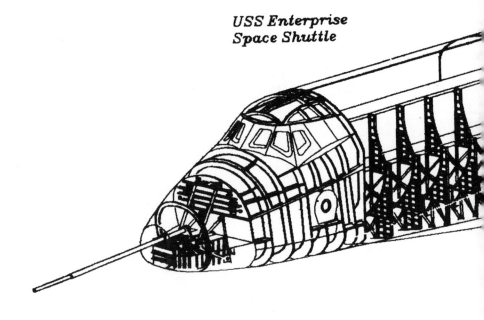

USS Enterprise
Space Shuttle

CAD plot sample:

space shuttle.   *Courtesy Versatec*

CHAPTER FIVE
APPLICATIONS

5.1   An Overview

CAD systems provide increased productivity for a large variety of user applications. A small sample is listed below.

- *Mechanical Product Design*
  Companies that manufacture products ranging in complexity from small glass bottles and containers to large trucks.

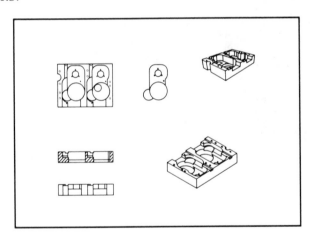

Courtesy Prime

- *Machine and Production Tooling Design*
  Companies that build their own production machines or tooling to specification. CAD can be used in designing molds, jigs, fixtures, and a broad spectrum of production machines, from machinery used to produce small

die cast electrical and plumbing fixtures to huge paper mill machinery.

- *Architectural*
  Firms that design small hospital facilities, large office complexes, or huge high-rise structures.

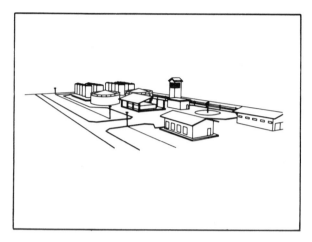

Courtesy Prime

- *Floor Plan Layout*
  Companies that need to make more efficient use of costly floor space, whether it is a small office or a large plant.

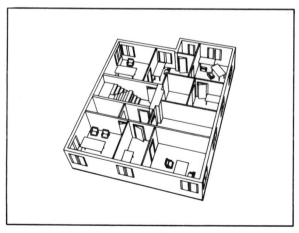

Courtesy Prime

- *Technical Illustration*

  Companies that produce two-dimensional and isometric mechanical illustrations, electronic diagrams, and other technical illustrations.

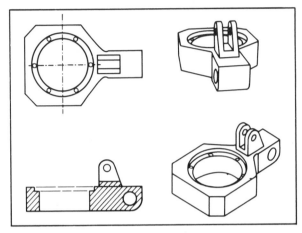

Courtesy Prime

- *Plant Engineering*

  Manufacturing firms that need to reposition plant equipment and locate personnel and safety areas to suit new product lines.

- *Electronic Product Design*

  Companies that produce automotive instruments, microprocessor based devices, or a whole complex system — analog, digital, or a combination of the two.

  We will use electronic product design as an example and take a detailed look at the use of a CAD system in the design of printed circuit boards.

5.2   A Detailed Look

The production of electronic products involves many distinct but related operations: circuit design and development, printed circuit board (PCB) or integrated circuit (IC) layout, mechanical design, manufacturing, assembly, and testing.

For the development department, there are special problems both in design and in preparing the necessary documentation for manufacturing. Each operation in development poses specific design problems: developing the circuit requires calculation of a theoretical solution, followed by breadboarding, testing, and refining; designing the printed circuit board entails overcoming spatial restrictions and layout constraints; designing the equipment housing requires consideration of cooling arrangements, protecting against shocks or vibrations, providing easy access for servicing and, at the same time, satisfying styling requirements.

To illustrate how a CAD system can be used in the development process, we will take a look at the design of a **printed circuit board.**

Designing a PCB using manual drawing or taping methods is a very tedious and time-consuming task. Having first prepared all the necessary information for the layout, a skilled drafter must find a suitable component placement solution within spatial restrictions and design constraints. The drafter then creates a tracking pattern for hundreds, possibly thousands, of connections, all the time working to a high degree of accuracy to avoid dimensional spacing errors. The completed design must be manually checked for spacing errors, for connectivity errors (by comparing it against the circuit diagram), and for artwork quality.

Finally, when the board is ready to be manufactured, drive tapes must be programmed for any NC manufacturing and testing machines to be used.

A CAD system provides a solution to the problems encountered in PCB design. The system speeds the design process and automatically produces manufacturing artwork, tapes, and documentation, enabling companies to benefit from increased productivity and reduced time scales for introducing new products into the market.

A schematic diagram provides a means of capturing all the data required to describe a particular circuit. It forms the basis for any electronic design project and is used thoughout the design process from development through PCB layout, to inclusion in service manuals.

A schematic drawing package can include many aids to ensure fast schematic layout. The circuit layout is carried out at a design station. The interaction with the graphics display is via the keyboard and tablet (with stylus). Options are displayed on the graphics screen and the designer selects the appropriate option from the menu. The designer is provided with various capabilities to assist his or her efforts thoughout the layout. The designer can ZOOM or WINDOW into selected areas of the drawing; different items can be set to different colors; and certain items can be made invisible to reduce the amount of data displayed and assist clarity.

Symbols may be called from the library and placed on the screen interactively using the tablet and stylus. The designer can move or rotate symbols as required. Subcircuits from previous work can be stored and used in the same way providing a good starting point for new schematics.

The designer can define the point-to-point connection pattern of the symbols interactively while working at the graphics display. The interconnections can be made with a choice of line widths or choice of colors to enable easy differentiation between say, voltage, ground, and signal connections.

Text, in various sizes, may be added by typing the text string on the keyboard. Once defined, the text can be positioned, rotated, and mirrored on the graphics display using the tablet and stylus.

Most systems allow the designer to reproduce repetitive areas of circuitry with ease. The designer creates the section of circuitry only once, and then defines it as a subdrawing. The subdrawing can then be positioned and replicated on the main drawing as required.

Once the schematic has been verified by the circuit engineer, data can be transferred to a PCB application package. Data transfer includes full details on components and can be back-annotated to the corresponding symbol or symbols on the schematic. More powerful systems allow you to verify the completed PCB against the schematic and automatically update the schematic drawing to ensure that both agree.

The PCB design process can be divided into the steps shown below. Within this basic framework, the actual methodology will vary slightly from system to system.

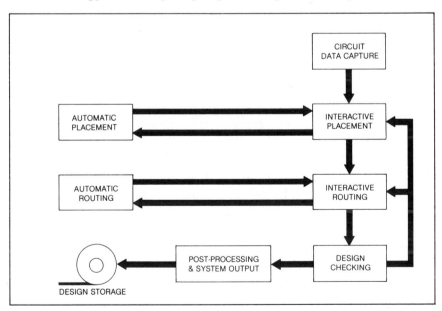

Printed circuit board design process.   *Courtesy Racal-Redac*

Routines are provided to move components interactively, rotate them, and fix them in position. All associated connections move with the component to enable fast assessment of location and rotation. Free text and component names can be manipulated in a similar manner to components, with the added ability for mirroring so that text can appear on either side of the board.

Interactive routing enables circuit connections to be converted to tracks and allows the designer to modify route paths created by automatic routers. Connections are displayed as straight point-to-point lines which can then be converted to a series of orthogonal or angled track segments using the tablet and stylus. Segments can be moved and swapped freely between layers, with via holes automatically created where required.

The interactive placement and routing routines allow boards to be designed from start to finish. However, all of the decisions and the implementation of those decisions are done by the designer. Much of the work required to do the placement and routing can be left to the computer.

Most PCB design systems provide the capability to do automatic component placement and automatic track routing. These routines are easy to use and provide significant reductions in design times.

Automatic component placement allows the designer to lay out integrated circuits and discrete components on user-defined grids. Routines are provided to swap components to improve the connection scheme. The designer has flexibility in using the placement routines; he or she can fix certain components in position and can restrict the routines to operate on particular sections of the board. In addition, the designer can interrupt the automatic routines to interactively place components as required.

The majority of circuit connections can also be converted to routes automatically. Automatic routing includes routines for handling power and ground connections, memory routing, and the remaining signal connections. More powerful systems include routers specifically designed for multi-layer work. They include facilities for minimizing the number of via holes and preventing vias from being inserted underneath integrated circuits. The automatic routing can be further enhanced by routines to do automatic gate and pen swapping.

Most systems include post-processors to link to a wide range of pen plotters, hard copy units, and photoplotters. The pen plotters and hard copy units enable fast check

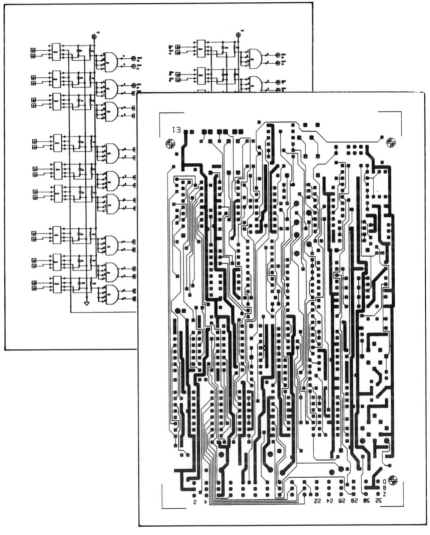

Printed circuit board schematic and artwork.   *Courtesy*
Gerber Systems

plots to be output at any stage in the design. Post-processors for photoplotters enable very high quality, one-to-one, or scaled artwork to be produced for all manufacturing artworks.

Output from the system does not end with manufacturing artworks. Data can be extracted from the same design data base to link to a wide range of NC equipment, including drilling machines, board profilers, automatic component insertion machines and automatic test equipment.

To complete the design cycle, the system can also provide design documentation with engineers' reports and full parts listings.

BOOKS ON CAD
OR RELATED TOPICS

Atkin, William Wilson. *Architectural Presentation Techniques.* Van Nostrand Reinhold, New York, NY, 1976.

Besant, C.B. *Computer-Aided Design and Manufacture.* Halsad Press, New York, NY, 1980.

Chance, David. *Computer Graphics —With 29 Ready to Run Programs.* Tab Books, Blue Ridge Summit, PA, 1981.

Chasen, S.H., and J.W. Dow. *The Guide for the Evaluation and Implementation of CAD/CAM Systems.* CAD/CAM Decisions, Atlanta, GA, 1979.

Daratech Associates. *Turnkey CAD/CAM Computer Graphics.* Cambridge, MA, 1981 (series of 3 books).

Demel, J., et al. *Computer Graphics.* Creative Publishing, College Station, TX, 1979.

Fetter, W.A. *Computer Graphics in Communications.* Engineering Graphics Monograph Series, McGraw-Hill, New York, NY, 1965.

Foley, James, D. *Fundamentals of Interactive Computer Graphics.* Addison-Wesley, Reading, MA, 1982.

Giloi, Wolfgang. *Interactive Computer Graphics: Data Structures, Algorithms, Languages.* Prentice-Hall, Englewood Cliffs, NJ, 1978.

Machover, C. *Display Systems: Computer Graphics*. The Optical Publishing Co., Pittsfield, MA, 1982.

Myers, Roy E. *Microcomputer Graphics*. Addison-Wesley, Reading, MA, 1972.

Negroponte, N., ed. *Computer Aids to Design and Architecture*. Petrocelli-Charter, New York, NY, 1975.

Neundorf, Norman. *Computer-Aided Drawing Using the Tektronic Graphic System*. Prentice-Hall, Englewood Cliffs, NJ, 1983.

Newman, W.M., and R.F. Sproull. *Principles of Interactive Computer Graphics*, 2nd Ed. McGraw-Hill, New York, NY, 1979.

Parslow, R.D., and R.E. Green, eds. *Advanced Computer Graphics: Economics, Techniques, and Applications*. Plenum Press, New York, NY, 1971.

Prince, M.D. *Interactive Graphics for Computer-Aided Design*. Addison-Wesley, Reading, MA, 1971.

Pruitt, Melvin L. *Computer Graphics: 118 Computer Generated Designs*. Dover Publications, New York, NY, 1975.

Ryan, D.L. *Computer-Aided Graphics and Design*. Marcel Dekker, New York, NY, 1979.

Voisinet, Donald. *Introduction to CAD*. McGraw-Hill, New York, NY, 1983.

COMPUTER REFERENCE BOOKS

Datapro Research Corporation. *Datapro Reports on Software* and *Datapro Reports on Minicomputers.* Delran, NJ.

Burton, Philip E. *A Dictionary of Microcomputing.* Garland Publishing, New York, NY, 1976.

Directory of Systems Houses and Minicomputer OEMs. Sentry Publishing, Hudson, MA.

Encyclopedia of Computer Science, 1st Ed. Van Nostrand Reinhold, New York, NY, 1976.

Myers, Darlene. *Computer Science Resources: A Guide to Professional Literature.* Industry Publications, White Plains, NY, 1981.

S. Klein Directory of Computer Graphics Suppliers, 1984-85 Edition. Technology and Business Communications, Sudbury, MA.

Sippl, Charles J. *Microcomputer Dictionary and Guide,* 1st Ed. Matrix Publishers, Champagne, IL, 1976.

Prenis, John. *Running Press Glossary of Computer Terms.* Running Press, Philadelphia, PA, 1977.

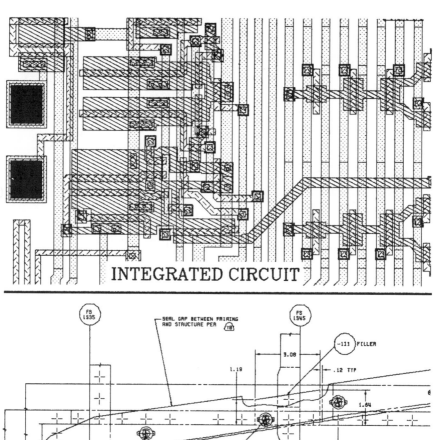

INTEGRATED CIRCUIT

MECHANICAL DRAWING

CAD plot sample.   Courtesy Versatec

GLOSSARY OF CAD TERMS

A

ACCEPTANCE TEST — A test for evaluating newly purchased hardware or software. The hardware or software must conform to pre-defined specifications.

ACCESS — To retrieve and use a specific program, or data.

ACCESS TIME — One measure of system response. The time interval between when data is requested from storage and when that data is displayed on the screen.

ACCURACY — Generally used to denote the number of digits to the right of the decimal point that can be used by a particular algorithm, program, or system.

ACRONYM — A word made from the first letters of words in a phrase. For example, CAD = Computer-Aided Design.

ADDRESS — The location of data or a program in storage.

ADDRESSABLE POINT — A position on the screen that can be specified by absolute coordinates.

ADDRESSABILITY — The number of points which can be displayed on the screen. A measure of picture resolution.

ALGOL — ALGorithmic Oriented Language. A high-level language.

ALGORITHM — A set of well-defined rules or procedures for solving a problem.

ALIASING — Straight lines appear as jagged lines on a raster display if the display has low resolution.

ALPHANUMERIC — Letters, numbers, and special characters, e.g., comma, period, semicolon.

ALPHANUMERIC DISPLAY — A display that shows letters, numbers, and special characters. It allows the designer to enter commands and to receive messages from the system.

ALPHANUMERIC KEYBOARD — A typewriter-like keyboard which allows a designer to communicate with the system.

ANALOG — Data is represented by linear movement rather than ones and zeroes as with digital.

ANNOTATION — Text, notes, or identification on a drawing, map, or diagram.

ANSI — American National Standards Institute. An association formed by industry and the U.S. Government to produce and disseminate drafting and manufacturing standards.

APPLICATION SOFTWARE — A computer program that performs a specific user task.

APT — Automatically Programmed Tools. A computer language used to program numerically controlled machine tools.

ARCHIVE — Placing infrequently used data in storage.

ARRAY — A set of elements or components arranged in a pattern, e.g., matrix.

ARTIFICIAL INTELLIGENCE — The ability of a computer to perform tasks normally associated with human intelligence, such as reasoning, learning, and self-improvement.

ARTWORK — A photoplot, photomask, pen plot, electrostatic copy, or positive or negative photographic transparency used to manufacture an IC, PC board, or other product.

ARTWORK MASTER — A highly accurate photographic representation of a circuit design used to fabricate the circuit.

ASCII — American Standard Code for Information Interchange. A standard for representing characters in the computer.

ASSEMBLER — The computer program that converts mnemonic instruction into equivilent machine language instruction.

ASSEMBLY LANGUAGE — A computer dependent language that corresponds one-to-one with the computer machine language instructions.

ASSOCIATIVE DIMENSIONING — Allows the value of a dimension to be automatically updated as the geometry changes.

ASSOCIATIVITY — The linking of parts, components, or elements with their attributes or with other geometric entities.

ATTRIBUTE — A non-graphic characteristic of a part, component, or element; for example: length, diameter, name, volume, use, and creation date.

AUTOMATED DESIGN SYSTEM (ADS) — Another term for a computer-aided design system.

AUTOMATED DRAFTING SYSTEM — Another term for a computer-aided drafting system.

AUTOMATIC DIMENSIONING — The CAD system computes the dimensions and automatically places dimensions, extension lines, and arrowheads where required.

AUXILIARY STORAGE — Storage devices other than the main memory. Also called peripheral storage. For example, disk drives.

B

BACK ANNOTATION — Data is automatically extracted from a completed PC board and is used to update the schematic. Information can also be back annotated into piping drawings and 3-D models.

BACKUP COPY — A copy of a file that is kept for reference in case the original file is destroyed.

BASIC — Beginner's All-purpose Symbolic Instruction Code. A high-level algebraic programming language.

BATCH PROCESSING — The running of a program or set of programs in a non-interactive mode.

BAUD RATE — A measure of the speed of signal transmission between the computer and the workstations. It is measured in bits per second.

BENCHMARK — A sample task or drawing used to test, compare, and evaluate the performance of various CAD systems prior to selection and purchase.

BETA SITE — A CAD site selected for testing a new hardware or software enhancement before its sale to other customers of the vendor.

BILL OF MATERIALS (BOM) — A listing of all the subassemblies, parts, materials, and quantities required to manufacture an assembly or to build a plant.

BINARY SYSTEM — The mathematical system used by all digital computers. The only two numbers used are 0 and 1.

BIT — A binary digit. The smallest unit of information that can be stored and processed by a digital computer. It can only be a 0 or 1. Computers are often classified by word size in bits, such as a 16-bit or 32-bit computer.

BITS PER INCH (BPI) — The density of data stored on a magnetic tape.

BOOT UP — To start up a system.

BOOTSTRAP — A routine whose first few instructions load the rest of the routine into the computer from storage.

BUFFER — A software program or hardware device used to hold data, when transferring data from one device to another, if there is a difference in the time it takes the devices to process the data.

BUG — A flaw in a software program or hardware design which causes erroneous results or malfunctions.

BUS — A circuit or group of circuits that provide a communications path between two or more devices.

BYTE — A sequence of eight bits that are operated upon as a unit.

C

CAD/CAM — Computer-Aided Design/Computer-Aided Manufacturing.

CARTESIAN COORDINATES — The distance of a point from any of three intersecting perpendicular planes; X, Y, Z coordinates.

CATALOG — The directory of files contained in storage.

CATHODE RAY TUBE (CRT) — A display device that creates images with a beam of electrons striking a screen.

CENTRAL PROCESSING UNIT (CPU) — The brain of a CAD system which controls the processing of information.

CHARACTER — A letter, number, or other symbol used to represent data. Symbols include the letters A through Z, numbers 0 through 9, punctuation marks, logical symbols, relational operators, and any other single symbol which may be interpreted by computer languages; a character is represented as a byte in the computer.

CHARACTERS PER SECOND (CPS) — The speed which a device, such as a printer, can process data.

CHIP — See integrated circuit.

COBOL — COmmon Business-Oriented Language. A high-level language oriented to business applications.

CODE — A set of instruction which may be in machine language, assembly language, or a high level language. Also may refer to an industry standard such as ANSI or ASCII.

COM — See computer output microfilm.

COMMAND — An instruction given to a processor using a menu and tablet, stylus, or alphanumeric keyboard.

COMMAND LANGUAGE — The language used by designers and drafters to operate a CAD system; varies with each system.

COMMUNICATIONS NETWORK — A number of systems tied together to transmit data.

COMMUNICATIONS LINK — The physical connection, such as a telephone line, from one system to another, or from one component to another.

COMPATIBILITY — The ability of a hardware module or software program to be used in a CAD system without modification.

COMPILER — A program that translates high-level language instructions to machine language instructions which can be understood by the CPU.

COMPONENT — A subassembly or part that goes into higher-level assemblies.

COMPUTER — A data processor that can perform arithmetic and logical operations.

COMPUTER-AIDED DESIGN (CAD) — The use of computers to assist in engineering, design, and drafting.

COMPUTER-AIDED ENGINEERING (CAE) — Using information from the CAD design data base to analyze the functional characteristics of a part, product, or system, and to simulate its performance.

COMPUTER-AIDED MANUFACTURING (CAM) — Using data from a CAD data base to control a manufacturing process, including numerically controlled machines, computer-assisted parts programming, computer-assisted process planning, and robotics.

COMPUTER ARCHITECTURE — The internal design of the parts of a computer system.

COMPUTER GRAPHICS — A generic term applied to any discipline or activity that uses computers to generate, process, and display pictorial images.

COMPUTER-INTEGRATED MANUFACTURING (CIM) — A totally automated factory in which all manufacturing processes are integrated and controlled by a CAD/CAM system.

COMPUTER LITERACY — A basic understanding of computers and their use.

COMPUTER NETWORK — Two or more interconnected computers.

COMPUTER NUMERICAL CONTROL (CNC) — Using a computer to store numerical control instructions generated by a CAD system controlling the machine.

COMPUTER OUTPUT MICROFILM (COM) — The image of a drawing plotted on 35mm film at a small scale by a beam of light.

COMPUTER PROGRAM — A set of software commands that instruct the computer to perform specific operations; often called a software program or software package.

COMPUTER WORD — A sequence of bits or characters treated as a unit.

CONFIGURATION — A particular combination of computer software, hardware, and peripherals.

CONNECT NODE — An attachment point for lines or text.

CONNECTION — The lines between pins, components, contacts, or circuits in printed circuit board and wiring diagram construction.

COORDINATE DIMENSIONING — A system of dimensioning in which points are defined as being a specified distance and direction from a reference point.

COPY — To reproduce a design in a different location on the screen or to duplicate a file and its contents.

CPU — See central processing unit.

CURSOR — A special character, such as a small cross, on the screen that follows every movement of the stylus, light pen, or joystick.

D

DATA — Elements of information.

DATA BANK — The total collection of information used by an organization.

DATA BASE — An organized collection of standard parts libraries, completed designs, documentation, and computer programs.

DATA ENTRY — Data entered by an operator from an input device such as a card reader, keyboard, or disk.

DATA MANAGEMENT — The control of access to information, information storage conventions, and the use of input and output devices.

DATA PROCESSING SYSTEM — A system that accepts information, processes it in a specific manner, and produces the desired results.

DEBUGGING — Detecting and removing programming errors (bugs) from programs.

DEDICATED — Assigned to a single function, such as a workstation used exclusively for engineering calculations.

DEFAULT — The predetermined value of a parameter that is automatically supplied by the system whenever that value is not specified by the user.

DELETE — To erase information from the computer's memory or from storage.

DELIMITER — A space, slash, asterisk, etc., that separates data within a continuous string.

DESIGN AUTOMATION (DA) — Using a computer to automate portions of the design process.

DESIGN FILE — The information in a CAD data base which relates to a design project.

DETAIL DRAWING — The drawing of a single part with all the dimensions and annotations necessary to completely define the part for manufacturing and inspection.

DEVICE — A hardware item such as a cathode ray tube, plotter, printer, or hardcopy unit.

DIAGNOSTICS — Computer programs that test a system or its key components to detect and isolate malfunctions.

DIGIT — Either 0 or 1 in binary notation; 0 through 9 in decimal notation.

DIGITAL — The representation of data as 1's and 0's.

DIGITIZE — To convert lines and shapes into digital form.

DIGITIZER — A table or tablet on which the designer moves a puck or stylus to selected points and enters coordinates for lines and shapes by pressing down the input button on the puck or stylus.

DIRECT NUMERICAL CONTROL (DNC) — Using a shared computer to distribute part program data to remote machine tools.

DIRECTORY — The location on the disk where the names of files and information about them are stored.

DISK DRIVE — The device that reads data from or writes data on magnetic disks.

DISK STORAGE — The use of magnetic disks as a storage device.

DISPLAY — The part of the workstation that shows the image of the data so that an operator can view it. Usually refers to a cathode ray tube.

DISTRIBUTED COMPUTER NETWORK — A group of computers that can communicate with each other.

DOCUMENTATION — The general description, user's manual, and maintenance manual necessary to operate and maintain the system.

DOWN — The term used to describe a computer or device that is not working.

DRUM PLOTTER — An electromechanical pen plotter that draws a picture on paper or film mounted on a drum using a combination of plotting head movement and drum rotation.

DUMB TERMINAL — A terminal that can only communicate with a host computer and cannot function in a standalone mode.

DUMP — To transfer all the data accumulated on the system during a given period to permanent storage.

DYNAMIC MOVEMENT — The ability to zoom, scroll, and rotate the image on the screen interactively.

E

EDIT — To change, add, or delete data or program code.

ELECTRICAL SCHEMATIC — A diagram of the logical arrangement of hardware in an electrical system, using standard component symbols.

ELECTROSTATIC PLOTTER — Wire nibs, spaced 100 to 200 nibs per inch, that place dots where needed on a piece of paper to generate a drawing.

ELEMENT — Basic geometric unit: point, line, arc, or circle.

EMULATION — The use of a computing system to execute programs written for another system.

ENHANCEMENTS — Software or hardware improvements, additions, or updates.

ERGONOMIC — Designed with the needs of the user in mind.

ERROR FILE — File generated during data processing to retain information about errors during the process.

EXECUTE — To carry out an instruction or perform a routine.

F

FAMILY OF PARTS — A collection of previously designed parts with similar geometric characteristics but differing in physical measurement.

FETCH — To locate data in storage and load it into the computer.

FIELD — A specific area in a string of characters or a record.

FIGURE — A symbol or a part which may contain other figures, attributes, and associations.

FILE — A named set of data on magnetic disk or tape. Also to transfer the contents of working storage to permanent storage.

FILE MANAGEMENT SYSTEM — A software system that provides control of input, output, physical storage, and logical relationships for data files.

FILE PROTECTION — The prevention of access to a file without proper authority and protection from accidental erasure of data within a file.

FILLET — A rounded corner or arc that blends together two intersecting curves or lines.

FINITE ELEMENT ANALYSIS (FEA) — The determination of the structural integrity of a part by mathematical simulation of the part and the forces acting on the part.

FINITE ELEMENTS — The subdivision of a complex structure into small pieces.

FINITE ELEMENT MODELING (FEM) — The creation of a mathematical model of a part for input to a finite element analysis program.

FLATBED PLOTTER — An electromechanical pen plotter that draws a picture on paper, glass, or film mounted on a flat table. The plotting head provides all the motion.

FLICKER — The flashing on and off of the image on the screen.

FLOPPY DISK — A flexible magnetic disk used to store data.

FLOWCHART — A graphical representation of the solution of a problem in which symbols are used to represent operations, data flow, and equipment.

FONT, LINE — Repetitive patterns used to make a line more easily recognized, e.g., a solid, dashed, or dotted line.

FONT, TEXT — An assortment of characters of a given size and style.

FORMAT — The specific arrangement of data for a list or report.

FORTRAN — FORmula TRANslation. A high-level language primarily for scientific applications that use mathematical formulas.

FUNCTION KEY — An area on the digitizing tablet or a key on a box or terminal that is used to enter a command.

FUNCTION KEYBOARD — A part of the workstation that contains a number of function keys.

FUNCTION MENU — The display or list of commands that the user can use to perform a task.

G

GLITCH — Minor, often temporary, malfunction of computer hardware or software.

GRAPHIC PRIMITIVES — Simple geometric shapes such as lines, circles, cones, cylinders, ellipses, and rectangles that can be used to construct more complex shapes.

GRAPHIC TABLET — Another term for a digitizing tablet.

GRAPHICS — Pictorial data such as points, lines, shapes, and drawings.

GRID — A matrix of uniformly spaced points displayed on the screen for exactly locating and digitizing a position or inputting symbols in the creation of a schematic.

H

HARD COPY — A copy on paper of what is shown on the screen which is generated with an on-line printer or plotter.

HARD DISK — A hard metal disk sealed in a disk drive and used for storage.

HARDWARE — The computer, disk, magnetic tape, cathode ray tube, and other physical components that comprise a system.

HIDDEN LINES — Line segments that would ordinarily be hidden from view in a 3-D display of a solid object because they are behind other items in the display.

HIERARCHY — A data structure consisting of different levels of sets and subsets such that every subset of a set is on a lower level than the data of the set.

HIGH-LEVEL LANGUAGE - A programming language that is independent of any given computer, easy to use, and permits the execution of a number of subroutines through a simple command. Examples are BASIC, FOR-TRAN, PASCAL, and COBOL.

HOST COMPUTER — The primary computer in a multiple computer operation.

I

INCHES PER SECOND (IPS) — The number of inches of magnetic tape that can be recorded or read per second or the speed of a pen plotter.

IN-HOUSE — Within an organization or company.

INITIALIZE COMPUTER — To set counters, switches, or addresses to zero or to other starting values at the beginning of a program or routine.

INITIALIZE DISK — To prepare a disk to store information in the format of the particular operating system being used.

INPUT — To enter data or a program into the system.

INPUT DEVICE — Devices such as graphic tablets or keyboards that allow the user to input data into the CAD system.

INPUT/OUTPUT (I/O) — Communications devices, as well as the process by which communication takes place in a CAD system.

INPUT/OUTPUT CHANNEL — The path for transmitting data in and out of the central processing unit.

INQUIRY — A request for information from the computer.

INSERT — To enter entities, figures, or information into a design that is on the display.

INSTRUCTION — Line of computer programming telling the computer what to do.

INSTRUCTION SET — All the commands to which a computer will respond.

INTEGRATED CIRCUIT (IC) — An electronic component which may vary in complexity from a simple logic gate to a microprocessor. An IC is usually packaged in a single substrate such as a slice of silicon. Also called a chip.

INTEGRATED SYSTEM — A CAD system that integrates the entire product development cycle — analysis, design, and fabrication — into a single system.

INTELLIGENT ROBOT — A robot that can make decisions by using its sensing and recognizing capabilities.

INTELLIGENT TERMINAL — A workstation that contains a built-in computer, usually a microcomputer or minicomputer, and can perform some processing in a stand-alone mode.

INTERACTIVE — Providing two-way instantaneous communication between a CAD system and its operators.

INTERACTIVE GRAPHICS SYSTEM — A CAD system in which the workstations are used interactively for computer-aided design and drafting. Often used synonymously with CAD.

INTERCONNECTION — In a drawing, the connection between one displayed entity or connection point on a component and another. On schematic drawings, interconnections are lines connecting elements.

INTERFACE — A hardware or software link that enables

two systems or a system and its peripherals to operate as a single, integrated system.

INTERFERENCE CHECKING — A CAD capability that allows plant or mechanical designers to examine a 3-D model and automatically pinpoint interferences between pipes, equipment, structures, or machinery.

INTERPRETER — A software program that converts high-level language instructions to machine language instructions.

I/O — See input/output

ISOMETRIC — A drawing in which the object is drawn from an oblique view so that the object appears as a solid object.

J

JAGGIES — The jagged or sawtoothed appearance of lines on the screen when it has low resolution.

JOB — All necessary computer programs, linkages, files, and instructions for a unit of work.

JCL — Job Control Language. A problem-oriented language used to express job requirements to an operating system.

JOYSTICK — A CAD data entry device that uses a hand-controlled lever to move the cursor manually on the screen so as to enter the coordinates of various points.

K

K — 1,024

KEYBOARD — Resembles a typewriter and is used to enter instructions to the computer.

KINEMATICS — A process for simulating the motion of mechanisms to study interference, acceleration, and forces.

L

LARGE SCALE COMPUTER — A computer with large internal memory capacity and multiple input/output channels. Such computers can process many programs concurrently.

LAYER DISCRIMINATION — The selective assignment of colors to a layer, or the highlighting of entities, to distinguish among data on different layers displayed on a screen.

LAYERING — Logically organizing data in a CAD data base on separate layers, each of which can be displayed individually or in any desired combination.

LAYOUT — A to-scale drawing of the physical components and mechanical and electrical arrangement of a part, product, or plant.

LIBRARY — A collection of symbols, components, shapes, or parts stored in the CAD data base as templates for future design work on the system.

LIGHT PEN — A penlike device used in conjunction with a vector-refresh screen that identifies displayed elements from the light source on the screen.

LINE PRINTER — A peripheral device that prints alphanumeric data one line at a time.

LINE SPEED — The rate at which signals can be transmitted over a communications line, usually measured in bauds or bits per second.

LOAD — To enter data into computer memory for later processing on the system.

LOCAL AREA NETWORK (LAN) — A communications network in which all of the computers and workstations are in the same general area or building.

LOG ON — To follow the procedure by which a user begins a workstation session.

LOG OFF — To follow the procedure by which a user ends a workstation session.

LOOP — A sequence of instructions that is executed repeatedly in the computer until stopped by an operator or some predetermined condition.

M

MACHINE — A computer.

MACHINE INSTRUCTION — An instruction that a computer can recognize and execute.

MACHINE LANGUAGE — The set of instructions, in the form of 1's and 0's, that are used directly by a computer.

MAGNETIC DISK — A flat circular plate with a magnetic surface on which data can be recorded and from which data can be read. The data can be randomly accessed.

MAGNETIC DRUM — A cylinder with a magnetic surface on which data can be recorded and from which data can be read.

MAGNETIC TAPE — A tape with a magnetic surface on which data can be recorded and from which data can be read. The data can only be sequentially accessed. The access speed is constrained by the location of the data on the tape, the speed of the tape drive, and the density of the data on the tape.

MAIN MEMORY — The principal data storage device of a computer system — an integral part of the computer. Generally just called memory.

MAINFRAME COMPUTER — A large-scale computer.

MANAGEMENT INFORMATION SYSTEM (MIS) — A system that can store, retrieve, process, and output data to help management in its decision-making functions.

MASS STORAGE DEVICE — A memory device that is capable of storing and communicating vast amounts of data.

MATRIX — A 2-D or 3-D rectangular array of identical symbols or entities.

MENU — A table of available commands, either on a digitizing tablet or on the screen, that can be selected instead of using the keyboard.

MEGABYTE — One million bytes.

MERGE — To combine two or more sets of related data into one set.

MICROCOMPUTER — A small, relatively low-cost computer that includes a microprocessor, memory, and all necessary interface circuits. Home or personal computers such as Apple, IBM PC, and TRS-80 are examples of microcomputers.

MICROPROCESSOR — A single integrated circuit that is the central processing unit of a microcomputer.

MINICOMPUTER — A computer that is between the mainframe computers and the microcomputers in size, power, complexity, and cost.

MIRRORING — Automatically creating a mirror image of a graphic entity on the screen by flipping the entity about an axis.

MNEMONIC — Short words that represent complete sentences or phrases of instruction.

MODEL — An accurate 3-D representation of a part, assembly, or plant designed on a CAD system and stored in the data base.

MODELING — Constructing a mathematical or analytic model of a physical object or system for analysis.

MODEM — MOdulator-DEModulator. A device that converts digital signals into analog signals for transmission over telephone lines. The analog signals are converted back to digital signals at the other end by another modem.

MODULARITY — The method of assembling a system by using components that can be replaced individually.

MONITOR — A display for computer output. Either monochrome or full color, a monitor is most often a cathode ray tube.

MOTHER BOARD — The large printed circuit board at the bottom of a computer to which chips, other boards, and components are attached.

MOUSE — A hand-held data entry device, about the size of a cigarette pack, which can be used without a digitizing pad. It can be used like a puck.

N

NC — See numerical control.

NESTING — Organizing design data into levels for greater efficiency in storing and processing repetitive design elements.

NODE — A computer or workstation connected to a local area network.

NUMERICAL CONTROL (NC) — The control of machine tools, drafting machines, and plotters by punched paper or magnetic tape encoded with the proper information to cut a part or draw a figure.

NUMERIC KEYPAD — A calculator-type numeric input device that is generally part of the keyboard.

O

OFF-LINE — Not connected to the system's computer.

ON-LINE — Connected to and under the direct control of the system's computer.

OPERATION — An action that a computer is instructed to perform, such as add, subtract, store, read, or write.

OPERATING SYSTEM — The software that controls the execution of computer programs and all hardware activity. Also called system software.

OPERATOR — The person who performs the input and output functions at a workstation.

ORIGIN — An X,Y or X,Y,Z coordinate from which all figures and entity locations are referenced.

ORTHOGRAPHIC — The method of making a layout, drawing, or map in which the projecting lines are perpendicular to the plane of the drawing or map.

OUTPUT — The end result of a process or series of processes, such as artwork, hardcopy, reports, and drawings.

OUTPUT DEVICE — Hardware, such as a printer or plotter, used to produce a copy of the results of the computer's processing operations.

OVERLAY — To position one or more drawings on top of another and view them simultaneously on the screen.

P

PAINT — To fill in a bounded figure on a display using a combination of repetitive patterns or line fonts.

PAN — To scroll the view of an object on the screen.

PAPER TAPE PUNCH/READER — A peripheral device that can read as well as punch a perforated paper tape.

PARALLEL INTERFACE — An interface that transfers several signals at once.

PARAMETER — A variable that controls the effect and usage of a command.

PART — A product, assembly, subassembly, or component.

PART PROGRAMMING LANGUAGE — A language that describes machining operations so that they are understood by computers or controllers.

PASCAL — A high-level programming language frequently preferred by computer scientists for its more logical structure and greater power.

PASSWORD — A unique string of characters that a programmer, computer operator, or user must enter to gain access to data.

PATH — The route that an interconnection takes between connections in printed circuit board design.

PATTERN GENERATION — The transformation of CAD integrated circuit design information into a format for use by a photo- or electron-beam machine in producing a reticle.

PC — Printed circuit or personal computer.

PEN PLOTTER — An electromechanical CAD output device that draws a picture on paper or film using a ballpoint pen or liquid ink.

PERFORATED TAPE — An input or output medium that uses punched holes along a continuous strip of nonmagnetic tape to record and store data.

PERFORMANCE, CRT — How well the cathode ray tube meets specifications such as screen resolution, display writing speed, internal intelligence, working area, accuracy, and precision.

PERFORMANCE, SYSTEM — How well a system meets specifications such as speed, capacity, accuracy, and the productivity ratio of CAD versus manual methods.

PERIPHERALS — Devices connected to a computer such as tape drives, disks, workstations, and plotters.

PERMANENT STORAGE — The location, outside the central processing unit, where completed data is stored, such as a disk or tape.

PHOTOPLOTTER — A output device that produces high-precision artwork on film for printed circuit board design and integrated circuit masks.

PIXELS — PICture ELements. Individual dots on a display screen that are illuminated to create an image. Pixels are evenly spaced on the display.

PL/1 — Programming Language/1. A high-level programming language used in a wide range of commercial and scientific applications.

PLOT — Drawing by pen or pencil of a design on paper or film to create a drawing.

PLOTTER — An automated device used to produce accurate drawings. Plotters include electrostatic, photoplotter, and pen.

POINT — An element that represents a single X,Y,Z coordinate.

POLAR COORDINATES — The two numbers that locate a point by (1) its distance from the origin and (2) the angle a line through this point makes with the X-axis.

POWER SUPPLY — A transformer that reduces voltage and changes AC to DC to provide electrical power to the computer.

PRIMITIVE — A fundamental graphic entity such as a vector, a point, or a text string.

PRINTED CIRCUIT BOARD (PC BOARD) — A board made of insulating materials and an etched pattern on which are mounted integrated circuits and other components required to implement one or more electronic functions. It is called printed circuit because the circuitry is connected not by wires but by copper foil lines, paths, or traces actually etched onto the board's surface.

PRINTER — An output device that copies data from a system onto paper.

PRINTOUT — Computer output printed on paper.

PROCESSOR — The hardware components that perform arithmetic and logic operations. Often called the computer.

PROGRAM — The complete sequence of instructions to the computer to perform a task.

PROGRAMMABLE KEY — A key that can be programmed to execute a complex series of commands.

PROGRAMMING — The design, writing, and testing of a program.

PROM — Programmable Read Only Memory. A read-only integrated circuit that can be programmed.

PROMPT — A message or symbol appearing on the screen that informs the user of a procedural error, incorrect input to the program being executed, or the next expected action.

PROPERTIES — Nongraphic entities which may be associated. Properties in electrical design may include component name and identification, color, wire size, pin numbers, lug type, and signal values.

PROTOCOL — The format of signals between two computer systems or between a computer and its peripherals that allows them to communicate.

PUCK — A hand-held input device that enables the user to digitize a drawing placed on the digitizer surface.

Q

QUALITY ASSURANCE (QA) — Used synonymously with Quality Control and Quality Engineering.

QUALITY CONTROL — The establishment and maintenance of standards to assure well-made products.

QUALITY ENGINEERING — The performance and interpretation of tests to measure product quality.

QUEUE — A waiting list of tasks to be performed or messages to be transmitted.

R

RANDOM ACCESS MEMORY (RAM) — A main memory storage unit that provides direct access to the stored information.

RASTER DISPLAY — A CAD workstation display in which the entire screen surface is a matrix of pixels and the image is scanned at a constant refresh rate. The bright, flicker-free image can be selectively written and erased.

RASTER SCAN — A line-by-line sweep across the entire screen surface to generate the image. The device can display a large amount of information without flicker.

READ ONLY MEMORY (ROM) — A storage device whose contents are not erasable.

REAL TIME — Immediate feed back to the user from tasks or functions executed by a CAD system. Immediate feedback through the workstation makes interactive operation of a CAD system possible.

RECORD — Related data processed as a unit.

REFRESH — Frequent automatic redrawing of an image on the screen to keep it bright. Selective erasing or editing is possible without repainting the entire image.

REFRESH RATE — The rate at which the image on a screen is redrawn, e.g., 30 times/second or 30HZ.

RELIABILITY — The amount of time a system is running with no problems versus the down time.

REMOTE TERMINAL — An input or output peripheral located at a distance from the computer.

REPAINT — To automatically redraw an image displayed on the screen.

REPLICATE — To generate an exact copy of a design on the screen at any location or scale desired.

RESOLUTION — The smallest spacing between two lines that will allow the lines to be distinguished visually on the screen.

RESPONSE TIME — The elapsed time from the completion of a command at a workstation to the display of the results at that workstation.

RESTART — To resume execution of an interrupted computer program.

RESTORE — To return a design to its original configuration after editing or modification.

ROBOTICS — The use of computer controlled robots to automate manufacturing processes such as welding, material handling, painting, and assembly.

ROM — See read only memory.

ROTATE — To turn a displayed image about an axis through a predefined angle.

ROUTINE — A computer program.

ROUTING — Placing the interconnects between components on a printed circuit board or integrated circuit.

RUN — To execute a program.

S

SATELLITE — A remote system, connected to a host system, that contains processors, memory, and mass storage to operate independently from the host.

SAVE — To transfer the data created at the workstation to a storage device.

SCALE — To enlarge or shrink an image without changing its shape.

SCHEMATIC — A not-to-scale diagram of an electrical circuit.

SCREEN — A computer display device; also called a monitor or cathode ray tube.

SCROLL — To automatically roll up on a screen, as on a spool, a message or drawing too large to be displayed all at once.

SECURITY — Safeguards and procedures that can be applied to computer hardware, programs, and data to assure that access to the system is controlled.

SELECTIVE ERASE — The deletion of portions of a design without repainting the entire screen.

SEMICONDUCTOR — A material such as silicon that conducts electricity and is used for the storage and transfer of computer data.

SERIAL INTERFACE — A connection that transfers data sequentially, one bit at a time.

SHAPE FILL — The automatic shading of an area on the screen.

SILICON — The basic material used in the manufacture of computer chips. See semiconductor.

SILK SCREEN — Artwork used to print component placement and identification information on a printed circuit board.

SIMULATE — To imitate the behavior of a finished part under various structural and thermal loading conditions.

SOFTWARE — The computer programs, procedures, rules, and instructions that control the use of the hardware.

SORT — To segregate items into groups according to specified criteria, e.g., to alphabetize.

SPLINE — A smooth curve between a sequence of points in one plane.

STORAGE — The physical device or location that contains all of the information on a CAD system.

STORAGE DEVICE OR STORAGE UNIT — A peripheral component in which data can be stored and later retrieved.

STORAGE TUBE — A type of cathode ray tube that retains an image continuously for a long time without redrawing. It allows no selective editing or erasing.

STRING — A sequence of characters such as a word or sentence.

SYMBOL — A set of primitive graphic entities, lines, points, arcs, circles, and text that are grouped together as a unit. Symbols may be combined or nested to form larger symbols or drawings.

SYNTAX — The set of rules that describe the structure of statements in a computer language.

SYSTEM — All of the people, machines, and methods needed to perform a specific task.

T

TABLET — An input device that a designer can use to digitize coordinate data or enter commands into a CAD system by means of a stylus or puck. Also called a digitizing pad.

TAPE DRIVE — The peripheral device that records and reads magnetic tape.

TELECOMMUNICATIONS — The transmission of signals over long distances between a computing system and remotely located devices by telephone, microwave, infrared link, or coaxial cable.

TEMPLATE — A commonly used component or part that serves as a design aid and can be subsequently traced instead of redrawn whenever needed. The CAD equivalent of a designer's template is a symbol in the symbol library.

TEMPORARY STORAGE — A location in memory for temporarily storing results of a program on the system until the results can be transferred to permanent storage. Also called working storage.

TERMINAL — A device equipped with a keyboard and some kind of display that sends and receives information over a communication channel to and from a computer.

TEXT — Letters, numbers, and special characters.

TEXT EDITOR — A program used to create and modify text on the system.

TEXT FILE — A file stored in the system that consists entirely of text.

THROUGHPUT — The work performed by a CAD system or a workstation during a given period of time. A quantitative measure of system productivity.

THUMB WHEELS — A CAD input device that uses a manually controlled vertical wheel for locating a coordinate on the Y axis, and a horizontal wheel for locating a coordinate on the X axis.

TIMESHARING — The concurrent use of a computing system by which two or more users can execute computer programs simultaneously, usually from remote terminals.

TOLERANCE — The allowed variance from a given nominal dimension.

TOOL PATH — A trace of the movement of the tip of a numerical control cutting tool that is used to guide or control machining equipment.

TRACKING — Moving a cursor across the surface of the screen with a light, stylus, or puck.

TRANSISTOR — An electronic switch that transmits a signal of either 1 or 0 to communicate information in binary machine language. A semiconductor device often made of silicon.

TRANSLATE — To change data from one language to another.

TRANSPORTABILITY — The ability to execute a program on different computers without major changes.

TREE — A method of file storage in which the file structure has a top level and one or more sublevels, which in turn may contain additional sublevels.

TURNAROUND TIME — The elapsed time between the start and finish of a task or project.

TURNKEY SYSTEM — A CAD system for which the vendor assumes total responsibility for building, installing, and testing all the hardware and software required to do a specific application or applications.

TUTORIAL — A message that is displayed to show the user how to perform a task.

U

UP — A term used to denote that the computer is working properly.

UPDATING — Changing a file by adding, modifying, or deleting information.

USER FRIENDLY — A CAD system (both hardware and software) that is easy to understand and operate.

UTILITY PROGRAM — A specific system software program such as a diagnostic program, a plot program, or a sort program.

V

VECTOR — A directed line segment that has magnitude and direction.

VERIFICATION — The computer's acknowledgment to a workstation user that a valid instruction or input has been received.

VERSION — A configuration control identifier that is changed whenever there are modifications or enhancements.

VIA — A hole in a printed circuit board through which a path from one layer or side is transferred to the other.

VIEW PORT — A user selected viewing area on the screen which frames the contents of a window.

W

WAFER — A slice of silicon from which a larger number of integrated circuit chips are produced.

WINCHESTER DRIVE — A combination of a disk drive and one or more hard disks permanently sealed in a case.

WINDOW — A portion or view of a design that is framed by a view port.

WINDOWING — Proportionally enlarging a figure or portion of a figure so it fills the screen or view port.

WIRE FRAME — A picture of a 3-D object displayed on the screen as a series of lines that represent the edges of its surfaces. This picture looks as if it were made from coat hangers.

WIRING DIAGRAM — A schematic representation of all circuits and devices that shows their interconnectivity.

WORD PROCESSING (WP) — The use of a special program to create, edit, store, display, and print text.

WORKING DRAWING — A detailed layout of components with complete dimensions and notes.

WORKSTATION — The hardware by which a designer interacts with the computer. Also called a terminal.

WRITE — To copy information from main memory to a storage device.

WRITE PROTECT — A security feature that prevents existing data from being erased by new data.

Z

ZOOM — The successive enlargement or shrinking of the image on the screen.

INDEX